Lakeland's Mining Heritage

The last 500 years

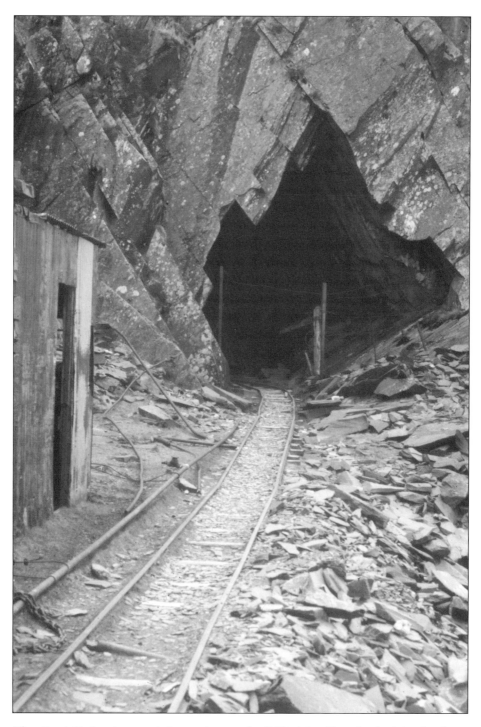

The Road End entrance at the eastern end of Honister Crag leads into the huge underground complex of the Honister and Kimberley slate mines. It was out of this entrance that much of the slate was brought in later years of operation of the mine. In 1986 Honister closed down but thirteen years later was brought back to life by a local entrepreneur who is working the mine again by traditional methods.

Photo: *Ian Matheson*

Lakeland's Mining Heritage
The last 500 years

Written and published by
Cumbria Amenity Trust Mining History Society

2000

Editor: Alastair Cameron

Photographic editor: Mike Mitchell

This publication has been part funded by a grant awarded to
Cumbria Amenity Trust Mining History Society
by the Millennium Festival Awards for All.

ISBN 0-9539477-0-X

Published by Cumbria Amenity Trust Mining History Society
The Rise, Alston, Cumbria CA9 3DB

Printed in Great Britain by
Black Bear Press Limited
King's Hedges Road
Cambridge CB4 2PQ

CONTENTS

FOREWORD

by John Hodgson
Lake District National Park Archaeologist

Like many of the upland areas of England that are now cherished for their 'natural' beauty, the Lake District was once a hive of industry with busy ironworks, mills, quarries and mines. The distinctive landscape of the Lakeland fells has in many areas been significantly shaped by mining and quarrying over a very long period. The winning of fine-grained rock from the central Lakeland fells for the manufacture of stone axes in the Neolithic period was the first example of human exploitation of the geological riches of the area that was to become so important in later periods. Although there may have been mining of metal ores in later prehistory and the Roman period there is as yet little evidence to support this. The first real indication of large-scale mining in the Lake District comes from documents of the early medieval period that record the mining of copper in the Newlands valley and lead in the Caldbeck fells. It is the mining activity of more recent times however, from the activities of the Company of Mines Royal in the late 16th century to the last gasps of mining in the late 20th, that have left the most visible remains in the landscape. These remains are now valued for the story that they tell about the past and in some cases have been judged to be of national significance and protected as Scheduled Ancient Monuments.

The general acceptance of the historical significance of mining sites is relatively recent and it is in large measure due to the activities of groups such as the Cumbria Amenity Trust Mining History Society (CATMS) that we now recognise their importance to industrial archaeology. This book builds upon the earlier CATMS publication *Beneath the Lakeland Fells* and is a welcome addition to the literature on the industrial past of the Lake District. It is also a testament to the time and effort that the authors and others have devoted to the exploration and study of the abundant mining remains of the area. The knowledge that has been derived from this investigation has often been of great assistance to the Lake District National Park Authority in fulfilling its role of protecting the special qualities of the area and has also resulted in collaboration over the conservation of mining remains.

The government has recently indicated that it intends to put the Lake District forward as a candidate for World Heritage Site status because of the special character of its cultural landscape. This book amply illustrates a key element of that landscape and will be of interest both to specialists and visitors to the area who wish to learn about one of the most important and visible aspects of the Lake District's past.

INTRODUCTION
by David Bridge

During the year 2000 as many as twenty million visitors are expected to descend on the English Lake District. Some will settle for the amenities of the towns, the museums, the garden centres, the lakes and water sports. Others will derive their enjoyment from touring the valleys while many will leave the busy roads, towns and villages and take to the hills in search of open spaces, fresh air and exercise or in pursuit of rock climbing. The more inquisitive will look around and ask themselves what course of events shaped the Lake District which we see today. They will be only too aware of the impact of the tourist industry. They will ponder on the pros and cons of the acres of forestry plantations, admire the ancient farmsteads and miles of dry stone walling – the hallmark of a long tradition of sheep farming in the fells – and will undoubtedly know something of the once thriving woodland industries of charcoal burning and wood turning. But wherever they set foot they will sooner or later chance upon evidence of another activity which reached its peak in Victorian times and still leaves its mark over the fells and in the woodlands in the form of spoil heaps and holes in the ground, ruined buildings and well-graded tracks – all of which are testimony to Lakeland's great ore mining and slate quarrying industries.

Tourism and forestry are relative newcomers to the Lake District compared with the farming of herdwick sheep which has been carried on at least since monastic times. But those early Cistercian monks of Furness also raised iron ore and produced the charcoal to smelt it and in doing so supported a tradition which had already been practised in the Lakeland valleys for centuries before them. Since the 13th century or even earlier mines of copper, lead and silver have played a major role in the mining scene and the discovery of a deposit of pure graphite or wad in Borrowdale brought international recognition to this part of the world. In more recent times the extraction of barytes and of zinc and tungsten ores have widened the field. Slate quarrying in the Lake District is known to date from at least the 13th century and it would be surprising if the Romans had not been aware of local slate and mineral deposits and exploited them, though no record exists to confirm this. What we do know however is that an important quarrying industry was underway 5000 years ago in neolithic times for the production of stone axe heads, evidence of which can still be found high up on the slopes of Pike o'Stickle and Scafell Pike.

Mining and quarrying are therefore an essential part of the Lake District history and over the years have provided work for many thousands of people creating wealth for the Lakeland dwellers at different periods in the past, and in the case of slate continue to provide employment to the present day. It is therefore important that what remains of these vital industries is preserved if their contribution to the development of this once remote corner of England is not to be forgotten.

The main purpose of this book is to show some of the remaining evidence of the mining and quarrying carried out in the

Lake District over the last 500 years, from the time of Elizabeth I when German expertise was brought in to exploit the copper deposits right down to the present day. While the surface remains are there for all to discover for themselves the extent of the underground workings is not often appreciated. It is hoped that the reader will be persuaded that every effort should be made to maintain access to this hidden world beneath the fells to give future archaeologists and mine historians the best possible opportunity to continue the study of this important aspect of Lakeland's heritage.

Yew Crag winding drum, Honister

LAKELAND'S MINING HERITAGE – IRON
by Richard Hewer and Alen McFadzean

The iron industry has slowly matured within the Lake Counties for centuries, with industrial growth spreading from the small bloomery and forge sites, coastal plateau workings and the narrow veins of the fells to the huge mining and iron smelting complexes of the late 19th and 20th centuries. The industry declined during the mid 20th century because of dwindling ore reserves, cheap foreign imports and the pressures of economic viability.

The mining areas were divided into well-defined regions. Major deposits occurred around Egremont, Cleator, Cleator Moor, Ennerdale, Eskdale, Millom and Ulverston, with numerous smaller deposits within the Lakeland fells – for example, Langdale, Coniston and Grasmere.

The Whitehaven region has evolved from several distinct groups of rock. The carboniferous limestone overlying the Skiddaw slate on the south-eastern side has in turn been overlaid by the coal measures in the north-west. The southern area is covered by the St Bees sandstone. The principal ore bodies occurred within the seven bands of the carboniferous limestone series, the latter having been subjected to varying degrees of earth movement and faulting whilst the iron solutions penetrated the fault lines from above and below. The resultant ore bodies formed large flats (bodies of solid ore) which connected with the bedding planes of the host rock, irregular bodies occurring as large swellings within the vein, or true veins or faults whereby the haematite solution followed the lines of weakness. The miners were forever optimists, for, just ahead of them, the vein could open out into a new and profitable shoot of ore.

Large, shallow deposits were extensively worked by the early miners. Development was rapid – easily worked deposits provided greater profits but with this ambitious drive came the dangers and disasters. Roof falls were commonplace; holing into abandoned workings and slides of disturbed ground were all part of the miners' way of life. In several instances, where all the ore had been removed from the flats, it was necessary to fill the large voids with waste rock and in some cases sand was blown into the cavities, leaving only heavily timbered shafts for access to the lower workings.

Several varieties of iron were mined. The most common type was compact, hard, massive and of a bluish-purple hue (hard blue) usually associated with the flats. Kidney or pencil ore was often found in irregular deposits in the first and second limestones. Specular ore was something of a rarity often found in cavities (loughs) and saved to be sold as specimens by the miners (a lucrative sideline). Lesser ores consisted of dark 'black' soft ore; smite ore (very greasy and highly coloured); muck or 'ring' ore.

Research and field work has shown that the deposits were exploited from Roman times. Several bloomery sites suggest operations by early British or Norse settlers. Many of the sites date from the late medieval period but could have obliterated earlier workings. The earliest documented evidence of mining within Egremont parish relates to Bigrigg Mine in 1179. The surface cover was shallow and the deposits easily exploited, probably as open casts. Between 1179 and 1635 the search for further deposits was intensified. During the later years a large, pure deposit of ore was discovered at Langhorn which, by 1709, when it was still being worked, had yielded over 21,500 tons of ore. As the miners searched for new deposits several ancient workings were discovered revealing wooden pumps, wooden spades and clay pipes. The workings could then be dated to between 1585 (introduction of tobacco) and 1602 when spades had metal tips fitted.

In 1784 Crowgarth Mine tapped a particularly rich body of 'hard blue' ore. 20,000 tons were transported to the Carron Foundry in Stirlingshire. After this date there followed a ten year slump in the iron trade which slowed development work in Cumbria. However, following this unsettled period the metal prices improved and mining gained momentum until the decline in the 20th century.

Advertisements often appeared in the local papers offering plots of land … "with great prospects of iron ore". Exploration within the Lakeland fells was spasmodic. The veins of haematite were small, rich, but often mixed with stone. Transport was difficult and iron prices were low. During the early 1840s prospectors tried any likely veins but it wasn't until the mid 1860s and early 1870s that serious attempts to work the lodes were instigated. The valley sides of Ennerdale Water received considerable attention, especially at the sites of ancient workings. The Crag Fell Mine (Ennerdale No 2) was the only producer of ore of any quantity. Meanwhile, Floutern Tarn (Red Gill Mine) received notoriety for the activities in share dealing by Faithful Cookson who was also associated with several other ventures in the area and in neighbouring Eskdale. The trials around Scale Beck and along the flank of Gale Fell provided a limited amount of ore which was sorted, cleaned, bagged and wheelbarrowed away!

The Kelton and Knockmurton mines were the only large producers of ore from the Skiddaw slate formation. The mines were owned by William Baird & Co, of Gartsherrie, Scotland, who had ventured south in search of quality ore for their blast furnaces. Between 1869 and 1913 over 1.25 million tons were raised, much of which was transported to their works, though some went to the Moss Bay and Harrington furnaces near Whitehaven and a little to the Midlands.

The mines of Eskdale have fortunately left us with the Ravenglass and Eskdale Railway. This was constructed solely to serve the mines and was nearly 'lost' when the workings closed down. Nab Gill Mine, further developed in 1870 by Whitehaven Iron Mines Ltd, worked the veins in the Eskdale granite. It produced roughly 8,000 tons per annum; however, tonnage declined after 1881. Gill Force and Gate Crag mines on the south side of the valley were the second major producer, and were worked by the South Cumberland Iron Company. A branch line from the Ravenglass and Eskdale Railway served the latter workings. Several small workings dot the slopes of the valley (e.g. Bann Garth and Christcliff). The iron ore was extracted by overhead stoping and removed from Nab Gill by way of an inclined tramway to the main line.

The upsurge in both coal and iron mining provided an impetus towards further development of the railway network. The small country lanes could not cope with the volume of traffic transporting ore to the ports and major rail headings. During the winter months the lanes became impassable, often deep in haematite slurry. Horses suffered leg and back injuries through falls and overloaded wagons. Prosecutions were brought against the owners by the RSPCA.

The railway companies quickly developed a programme of line expansion, welcomed by many but not all. 1845 saw the Maryport to Carlisle Railway and during the following year the Dalton to Kirkby line became operational. The Whitehaven to Ravenglass line opened in 1849 and was extended to Foxfield in 1850. By 1857 the Whitehaven to Egremont and Frizington line was completed. The line was extended to Marron in 1866 where it formed a junction with the Cockermouth and Penrith Railway. The Furness Railway Company constructed an extension from Egremont to Sellafield in 1869. Previously, ores had to be shipped by sea from Whitehaven. 1875-76 saw the opening of the Ravenglass and Eskdale Railway with the Cleator and Workington Junction Railway in 1878.

The Railway companies, during the early 1870s, adjusted their carriage rates. Bairds, of Kelton and Knockmurton mines, were not happy with the new arrangements and approached the Cleator and Workington Junction Railway who agreed to build a connecting branch from Distington to Bairds' mineral railway at Rowrah. This line was known as Bairds' Line and had gradients which were described as 'ferocious'.

The remains of mineral lines and branches still survive, silent, overgrown, and water-logged – cuttings full of refuse, bridges raided for their stones. Many lines led chequered lives, none more so

than the Ravenglass and Eskdale Railway which within seven months lost the traffic it was constructed for and yet, a hundred and twenty five years later, still survives.

The Rowrah and Kelton Fell Mineral Railway was surveyed as a simple branch line to Bairds' mines; however, the planned route aroused interest in possible extensions and alterations towards the infant mining ventures in the fells. Various schemes were suggested, for example in 1871 an extension was envisaged from Knockmurton to Red Gill Mine (Floutern Tarn) where a stationary steam engine would lower the bogies of ore down an incline to the line. A variation of this plan adjusted the track from 3 foot to 2 foot gauge, double tracked and suitable for carrying bogies containing 12 cwts of ore each. Another alternative included a tunnel a quarter of a mile in length.

A scheme suggesting a route from Cockermouth through the Vale of Lorton (passing the Scale Hill Hotel) by way of the

5

Mosedale Beck valley and travelling along the flank of Gale Fell towards Scale Beck Mine (eleven miles and estimated at a cost of £120,000) met fierce local resistance which took the proposers by surprise. But not so in 1881, when it was proposed to take a branch line from the Rowrah and Kelton Fell Railway at Kirkland down to the head of Ennerdale Water by way of a large bridge over Croasdale Beck. The aim was to tap the supply route from the iron ore mines in the Ennerdale valley.

The Rowrah and Kelton Fell line was approved and the other proposals were abandoned. How the Lakeland scene could have changed if all the schemes had materialised. The line became operational in 1877, serving the mines until 1913 and Kirkland village until 1927. One of the saddle tank locos still survives, built specifically for the line by Neilsons of Glasgow and named 'Kelton Fell'. The engine can be seen at the Scottish Railway Preservation Society museum in Bo'nes Railway, Falkirk. The engine was built in 1876 and had a most eventful career. (see The History of the Kelton & Knockmurton Iron Mines by R E Hewer, *British Mining No 36*)

Furness and Hodbarrow

The haematite ore fields of Furness are bordered to the north by Silurian slate and to the south by permo-triassic sandstone, the host rocks being a succession of six distinct limestones deposited during the Carboniferous period. Unlike the non-ferrous mineral veins of the nearby Lakeland mountains, the haematite lodes of Furness conform to no particular pattern. Only in certain instances – mainly in the southern and eastern areas of the ore field –

do they manifest in true mineral vein form, the deposits of the north and west being in highly irregular masses.

Large-scale mining has taken place at a number of locations between the towns of Barrow and Ulverston. The major ore deposits were situated at Askam, Roanhead, Park, Yarlside, Stank, Mouzell, Crossgates, Marton and Lindal; with peripheral deposits at Urswick, Stainton, Pennington and Plumpton.

Across the Duddon Estuary, in the carboniferous limestone between Millom and Haverigg, ore was mined at Hodbarrow from one of the largest bodies of haematite ever discovered. Three miles to the north-west an outlying vein in the Wicham Valley yielded haematite ore from the fault between the limestone and the older Skiddaw slate.

Just when mining began is a point open to conjecture. Archaeological evidence determines that ore was smelted in the vicinity of Urswick during the Iron Age by indigenous Celts.

During the mediaeval period the economic structure of Furness was controlled by a handful of landed families and the Cistercian monks of the Abbey of Saint Mary. The monks commenced mining at a place called Orgrave, on the outskirts of Dalton, prior to 1235, and by 1300 had developed several locations for the winning of ore, mostly in the vicinity of Dalton. These initial ventures were probably open cast workings, exploiting shallow layers of mineral worked with ease once the overlying boulder clay pinnel had been removed.

In 1396, William de Merton bequeathed land surrounding the villages of Marton, Dalton and Orgrave to the Abbot and Covenant of the Blessed Mary of Furness, so that the monks could "throw out and raise all manor of mineral or ore there found out of the mines". The wording suggests that techniques had changed, that the monks were, by this period, digging deeper and toiling in pits beneath the earth.

The smelting of the haematite was achieved using methods similar to the crude techniques employed by the ancient Celts. Ore was heated in primitive hearths called bloomeries – small clay domes in which charcoal burnt to a temperature sufficient to render the ore malleable, or soft enough to allow the impurities to be beaten out by the forgeman. The abundance of suitable woodland for the provision of charcoal, rather than the proximity of haematite, usually dictated the siting of the bloomeries. It was not uncommon for ore to be transported to the banks of Coniston Water (along Iron Yeat) during the monastic period, and smelted where both charcoal and water were plentiful.

Towards the close of the monastic period this traditional mode of smelting was superseded by the stringheath, a slightly larger version of the bloomery but with the addition of a bellows mechanism powered by a water wheel. A further refinement was the bloomsmithy, where the water wheel powered a mechanical forge hammer as well as applying the blast to the hearth. The 17th century saw the gradual domination of the bloomsmithy as the main means of converting raw haematite into marketable wrought iron. But it was the introduction of the charcoal blast furnace to the valleys of south Cumbria which revolutionised the process and stimulated local mining into a vigorous and highly competitive industry.

The first charcoal blast furnace was built at Cunsey in 1711, close to the shores of Windermere, by a group of Cheshire businessmen. The local ironmasters reacted with remarkable celerity and during the same year erected a furnace at Backbarrow, on the River Leven. Such was the impact of these two smelters on the local economy, that, within 40 years, a number of similar furnaces had sprung up at Leighton, near Carnforth, Duddon Bridge, near Broughton-in-Furness, Nibthwaite, at the foot of Coniston Water, Low Wood, on the banks of the Leven, Newland, near Ulverston, and Penny Bridge on the River Crake. The success of the ironmasters is put into perspective, along with the rate at which the iron industry, as a whole, expanded by the fact that several charcoal blast furnaces were established in the North of Scotland where charcoal was plentiful to which Furness haematite was shipped for processing.

The iron industry was further stimulated by the introduction of more advanced smelting and refining techniques during the 19th century, but the main boost – Furness' introduction to the Industrial Revolution – occurred in 1711 on the wooded banks of England's largest lake.

Alongside these developments in smelting, a similar pattern in mine ownership began to emerge. With the gradual adoption of the stringheath and the bloomsmithy came the farmer entrepreneurs and the landed ironmasters, filling the vacuum left by the monks. Mining methods were crude, development restricted to narrow strip fields and complex field boundaries. And with the charcoal blast furnaces came the mining companies, organised bodies of local men and outsiders looking for opportunities in a land rich and red with iron ore. By the mid 19th century the ore fields had been apportioned into definitive mining royalties leased by a variety of companies, some retaining their traditional landed routes, others captained by experts trained in the hard rock mines of Cornwall.

John Bolton, author of *Geological Fragments of Furness and Cartmel*, gives us a unique insight into the cramped though incredibly industrious mines around Dalton in 1869.

This hill [High Haume] is a favourable site for a view of the surrounding district, and before we descend let us examine some of its physical features. Before us is the real California of Britain – the great haematite iron ore district of Furness – some of the principal mines forming a semicircle at the base of the hill. Commencing our review at the Northwest, we have first, the new mines of Messrs Kennedy Brothers, on the Askam estate; almost adjoining these the splendid mines of Messrs Schneider, Hannay and Co (this firm has now become the Barrow Haematite Iron and Steel and Mining Co), at Park; close to which are the Roanhead mines of Kennedy Bros. Glancing round the foot of the hill we find Elliscales, Messers Ashburner and Son; Butts Beck, Ricket Hills, Cross Gates, J Rawlinson Esq; the Ure Pits, Ulverston Mining Company; Mausell Mines, Messers Schneider, Hannay and Co; all skirting the base of High Haume, and constituting a circle arc of 180 degrees, with a radius of half a mile. Having found so much material of igneous origin at High Haume and Haverslack Hill, all these extensive mines being so near, we have been very particular in our description as it will naturally form an element in considering the formation of our haematite ore. Besides the above, there are the mines of Schneider, Hannay and Co at Old Hills, Whitriggs, and Marton, all within half a mile of the base of Haverslack Hill, which, as stated before is principally composed of amygdaloid. There are also mines at Carrkettle, of J Rawlinson, and the splendid mines of Lindal Moor, Whinfield, Gillbrow, and Whitriggs Bottom, of Messers Harrison, Ainslie, and Co; and at Lindal Cote, those of the Ulverston Mining Company; also at Dalton, those of J Denny and Co, and J Rawlinson; and near Highfield House, those of J Clegg Esq. All these mining works are within a mile and a half of High Haume; besides about a mile further we have the Ulverston Mining Co's at Stainton, Bolton Heads, Stone Close, and California; and Mister Wadham's at Crooklands; and Messrs Schneider, Hannay and Co's at Newton. Perhaps we have omitted some but we shall return to this subject.

Mining methods varied considerably across the Furness and Hodbarrow ore fields. In the narrow mineral veins around Urswick and Stainton, traditional methods of stoping were employed. In the veins, cross-veins, and ore-flats of Whitriggs – where the ore tended to mass in irregular pockets between the limestone bedding planes and natural rock fissures – the ore was systematically robbed, allowing the roof to collapse and reveal more ore. In the gigantic ore bodies (sops) of Park, Roanhead, Askam, Mouzell, Elliscales and Lindal Moor, top slicing became widely adopted, a method similar to the board and pillar system of mining coal, the difference being that the pillars were also removed, allowing the roof to crush down on the sole while another 'slice' was being worked underneath.

Top slicing required immense quantities of timber to support the working drifts, so in favourable conditions where the ore was harder the pillars were left unworked over a series of slices, creating large chambers with roofs supported by columns of haematite. The ore in the supporting pillars was exploited at a later date when the chambers had collapsed and subsidence crushed the ore to a friable mass.

The life expectancy of trial shafts under these conditions was short, and those sunk directly on the sops were quickly swallowed. The more permanent engine shafts tended to be situated on firmer ground but even these did not entirely escape the distortion caused by the ever encroaching subsidence.

The Hodbarrow deposit was, like the sops of Furness, large and irregular, though more akin to the flat deposits of the Egremont area in geological make-up. Top slicing was employed prior to 1922, but problems with subsidence and the close proximity of the sea brought about a change in policy and the adoption of bottom slicing. Ore was removed in slices from the sole of the deposit and the resultant voids filled with a slurry mixture of water and sand to prevent instability.

Water was a problem in the Furness mines. With the country rock being carboniferous limestone, underground 'runners' and 'feeders' were plentiful. On more than one occasion complete mines were washed out and the pumps overcome when subterranean watercourses were breached. Periods of sustained rainfall could flood certain pits within hours. The reports of the local mine inspectors give a fascinating insight into the extent of the problem, one of the most frequent comments being "the water's in".

Cornish beam engines were installed at Eure Pits (Dalton), Lindal Cote, Back Guards (Lindal), Whinfield (Lindal), Park, Roanhead, and Stank. Across the Duddon estuary there were Cornish engines at Hodbarrow, while Wicham Mine boasted two of the largest beam engines in the country at that particular time (1889-95). Horizontal pumping engines were common throughout the district, while during the early years of the 20th century several companies resorted to electrification as a means of improving their de-watering systems.

After the peak years of the 1870s and 1880s, decline was hastened by the gradual exhaustion of some of the older pits and the import of cheap iron ore from other countries, notably Spain. In Furness, the last big pit – Woodbine Pit at North Stank – closed in 1946. The end came in 1960 when the Margaret Mine, and inclined drift in Henning Valley, Lindal, was bought out by a larger concern and subsequently closed.

Hodbarrow Mine continued in production until March 1968 when its greatly reduced work force of a hundred and three men was laid off, bringing to an end haematite mining in the south of the county. Now, in the year 2000, just one working iron ore mine remains in Cumbria – the Florence Pit at Egremont.

Two Hodbarrow miners, Les Fell and Ron Dawson, push a wagon of ore towards the pit cage of Moorbank Shaft at Hodbarrow in September 1963. Less than five years later these extensive mines were closed with the loss of 88 jobs. The Hodbarrow mines were a source of high grade haematite for over 100 years and yielded almost 300 million tons of ore.

Photo by permission of the *North West Evening Mail*

The Millom Ironworks complex and Devonshire Road look impressive when viewed from the air. This photograph was taken in 1969 a few months after closure in September 1968 with the loss of 600 jobs and shortly before the works were dismantled. The ironworks were the town's largest employer and following closure Millom was plunged into serious economic crisis.

Photo by permission of the *North Western Evening Mail*

The Derby No 1 Pit, situated in Moor Field, Marton, was worked by a steam winding engine installed on the old Rawlinson Shaft in 1906. Prior to this date ore was raised by horse gin and kibble. The kibbles were loaded at the face and then transported by 'whitechappels' (above) to the foot of the shaft, where they were hitched to the rope and hauled to grass. The Derby No 1 Pit was sunk in 1886 and closed for the last time in March 1914.

Photo: *Alen McFadzean*

For many years the B.30 Pit, one of Furness' most notorious pits, was Lindal Moor's main producer. Sunk during the 1850s, and known originally as Whitriggs Gin Pit (and more evocatively, the Old Peru), its three haulage levels gradually penetrated into the cross-veins of Henning Valley, the Waste workings at Marton and the rich mineral ground of the Main Vein. Two thirds of the pit are now under water. This photograph was taken during a dry summer in the tramming level called Top Height, which, as the name implies, was the highest level of the B.30 workings. For most of the year the Top Height is totally submerged – only when the water level falls can access be gained through the workings of the B.45 Pit at Marton to the silent chambers of the Old Peru. The B.30 Pit closed on October 10th 1914.

The Stank iron mines of the Barrow Haematite Steel Co, photographed in 1879. In the centre of the picture is Stank No 1 pit, complete with Cornish pumping engine and sheer-leg capstan (the tallest frame with sheave wheel), used for lowering replacement sections of pit-work, the great reciprocating rods which activated the pumps at the foot of the shaft. The two winding engines are situated in the building on the extreme right; again these are beam engines, but of the rotary variety, with winding crank fitted to the beam ends. To the immediate left of No 1 Pit is Stank No 2, a pumping shaft with balance bob connected to the pit-work to counter the weight and ease the load on the engine. On the brow of the hill is Stank No 5 Pit and, in the far distance, Yarlside No 11, near Furness Abbey.

13

The Burlington Pit, Park Mines, Dalton in Furness in 1879. The pit shaft eventually reached a depth of 124 fathoms (over 700ft) in 1896 and contained four miners' cages. The Cornish beam engine shown in the photograph was installed in 1856 and worked for 74 years until it was replaced by electrical winding machinery.

The shaft of Blackguards Pit, Lindal in Furness was sunk in 1860 and was in operation for over 50 years. This photograph was taken in 1908, three years before the mine closed. The substantial Cornish beam engine was installed by the Barrow Haematite Steel Company to cope with the large flow of water which came from the higher workings of Henning Valley.

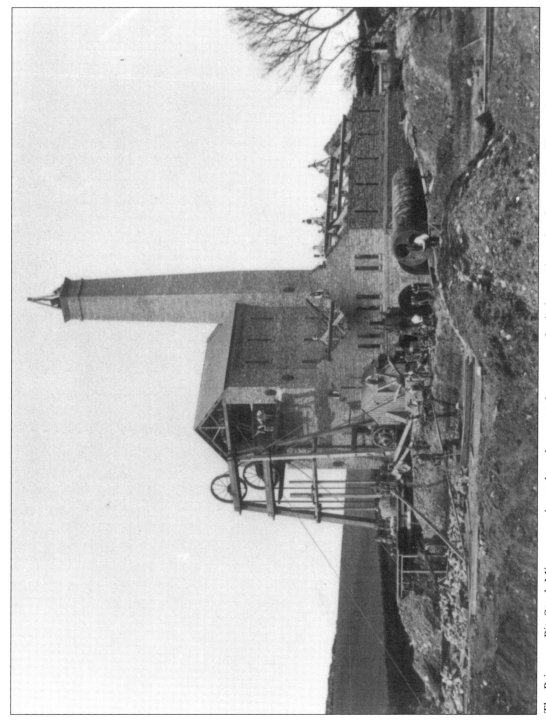

The Primrose Pit, Stank Mines, was situated on the county's most southerly haematite vein, close to the village of Newton, between Barrow and Dalton. The shaft at the mine was sunk to a depth of 85 fathoms and measured 15ft by 9ft. It was equipped with twin cages. The Stank Mines were closed in 1901. The photograph shows Primrose Pit during the period of its construction.

Duddon Furnace was erected in 1736 by the Cunsey company, of Cunsey ironworks near Windermere. Ore was shipped from Furness and off-loaded downstream of the smelting site, in the Duddon estuary. The furnace was taken over by Harrison, Ainslie & Co of Newland Furnace in 1828, and continued to produce pig iron until 1836. The blast furnaces of Cumbria were sited close to the coppice woodland rather than the mining areas to take advantage of the charcoal supplies. The site has been renovated in recent years, the furnace stack and associated buildings being reconstructed with authentic materials. To the right of the picture, the lintelled blowing arch looks out onto the bellows floor and waterwheel pit.

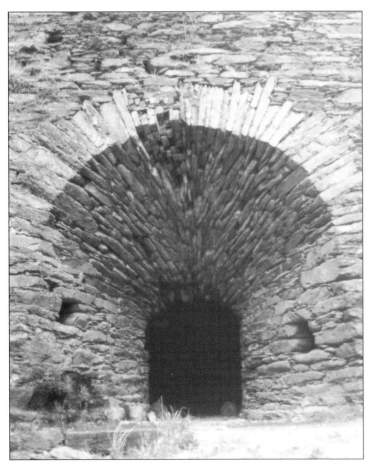

The casting floor is situated on the south side of the furnace stack. Beneath the almost perfect symmetry of the slate arch, molten iron once poured along a gutter in the earth floor to a series of moulds. The term 'pig iron' is derived from this process, for the moulds had the appearance of piglets feeding off the mother sow.

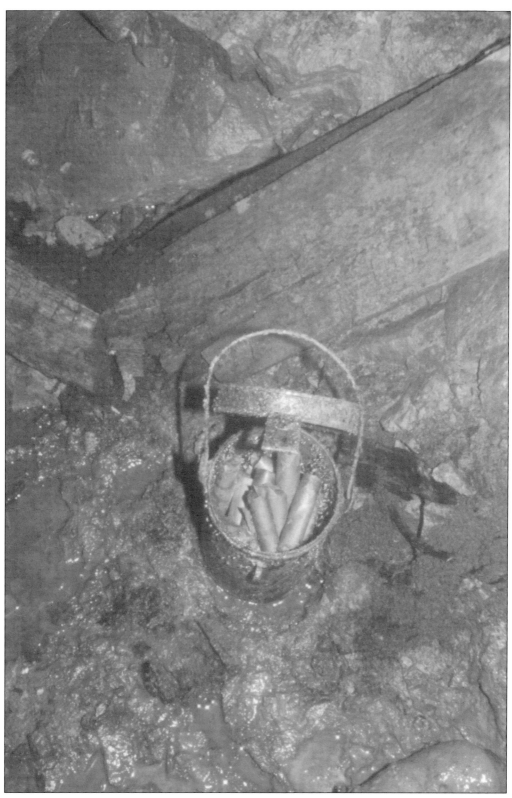

In a small side-drift off the main level of Whitriggs Iron Mine, Lindal in Furness, explorers discovered an alarming artefact. This explosive bucket was found still holding several sticks of dynamite. It was one artefact that was left where it was!

Photo: *Richard Hewer*

There are a number of old iron mines within the Lake District National Park, several of which are in the Eskdale Valley. This photograph of No 3 Level at Gill Force Iron Mine, Eskdale, shows the derelict state of these workings. The level leads to a collapse from the surface.

Photo: *Richard Hewer*

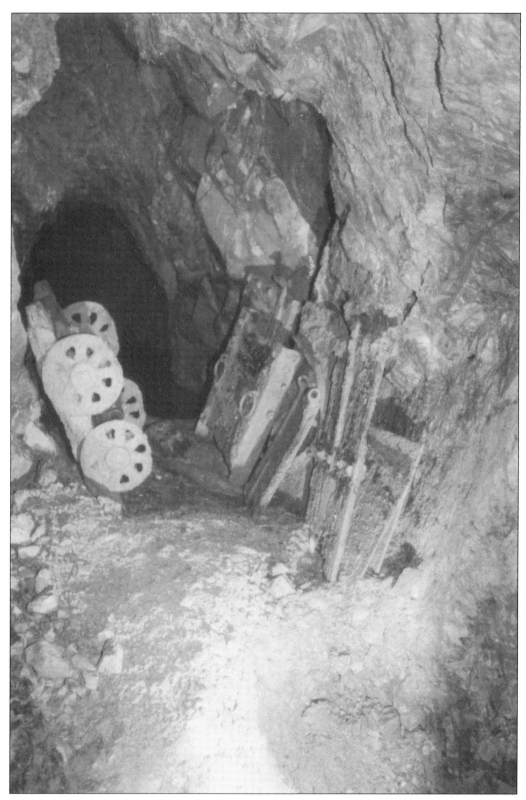

This dismantled ore wagon was discovered in the upper workings of No 1 and 2 veins at the Knockmurton Iron Mine. The wagon was designed to be stripped down easily for carrying to other areas of the mine. The side panels are propped against a two foot wide vein of kidney ore.

Photo: *Richard Hewer*

A worked out ore flat in the Guttersby No 3 Pit, Bigrigg, near Whitehaven. Here the entire ore body has been removed and square pillars of deads and timber constructed to support the roof. The ore flats were sandwiched between the layers of the carboniferous limestone, the angle of dip corresponding to that of the country rock.

Photo: *Anton C P Thomas*

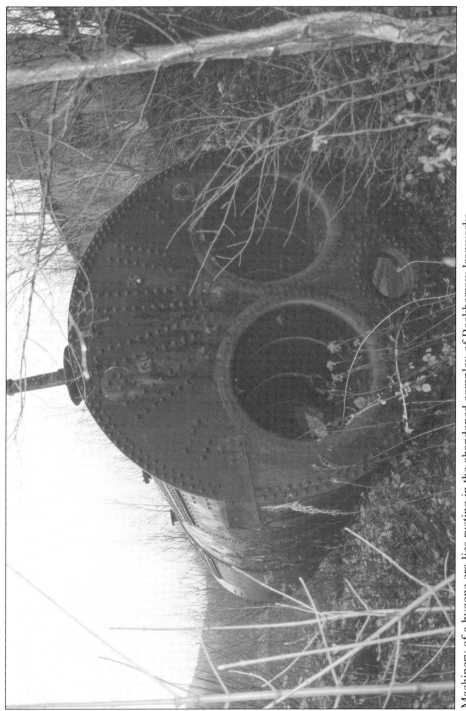

Machinery of a bygone era lies rusting in the abandoned complex of Backbarrow Ironworks.
On this page the photograph shows the Lancashire boiler which provided steam for the horizontal steam engine. The engine itself is photographed on the next page and worked the bellows which provided the blast necessary for the raising of the furnace to a temperature suitable for converting haematite ore to pig iron. Originally, when the Backbarrow furnace was constructed in 1711, the bellows were powered by a waterwheel which was situated in a wheel-pit behind the present engine house.
Backbarrow, along with Cunsey, is Cumbria's oldest charcoal blast furnace. Other furnaces were established at Newland, Duddon, Penny Bridge, Nibthwaite, Low Wood and Leighton.

Photos: Max Dobie

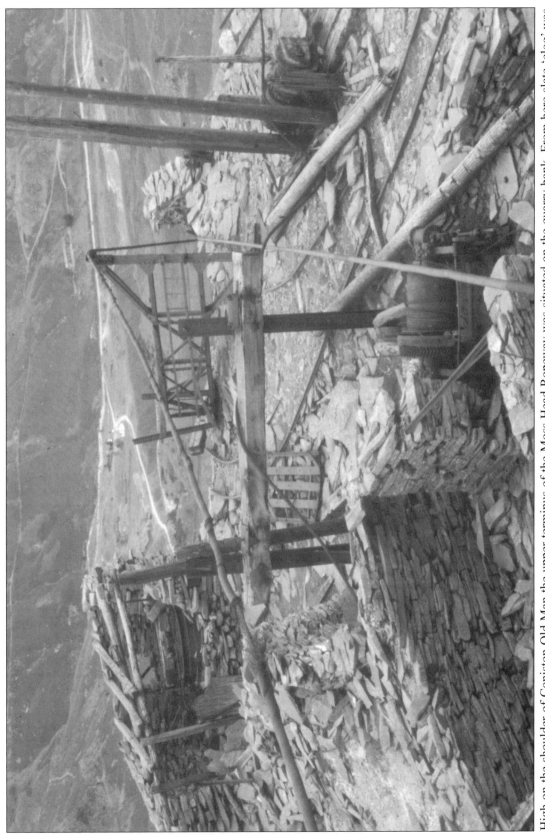

High on the shoulder of Coniston Old Man the upper terminus of the Moss Head Ropeway was situated on the quarry bank. From here slate 'clog' was lowered down the mountain to Saddlestone, the main processing bank of the Old Man Quarries.

Photo: *Mike Mitchell*

This more general photograph of Moss Head shows the collapsed pylons that once carried the static ropes and also the brake house in which the operator controlled the descent of the ropeway flights. When this photograph was taken, on a sunny May morning, it was raining in Coniston.

Photo: *Alastair Cameron*

Kidney ore, a form of high-grade haematite, photographed in the Florence Mine, Egremont. Florence is still being worked and is Europe's last remaining deep ore mine. Its haematite ore is the purest in the world and is still in demand for surgical instruments and as a paint pigment and for cosmetics.

Photo: *Ken Geddes*

Within the Gutterby Iron Mine the roof of this chamber is supported by the timber and drystone packs on the right. Just to the left of the packs a raised wagon way runs further into the workings. Exploration in this part of the mine is limited to periods when the water table falls to a low level, as is clearly apparent by the wet slime of iron ore covering the floor and walls.

Photo: *Richard Hewer*

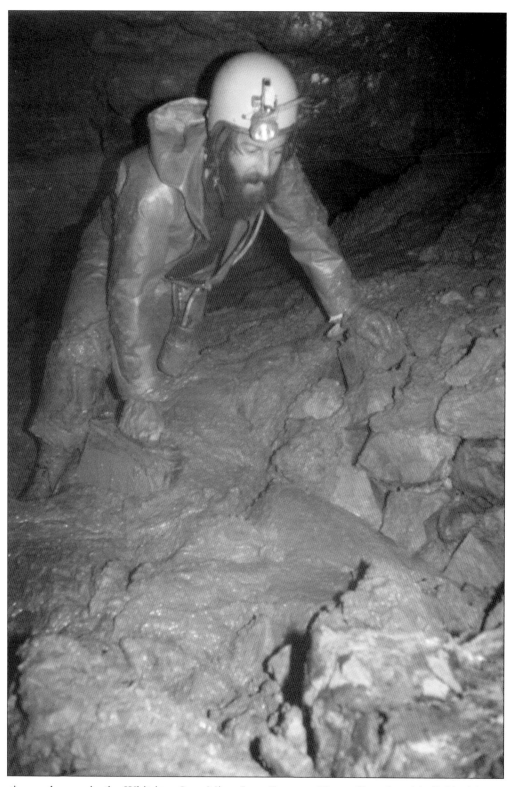

Exploration underway in the Whitriggs Iron Mine, Low Furness. The well-equipped individual has entered a small flat running in off the main horse level. As in most iron mines in this area, haematite slurry persists all around. Exploration results in stained clothing, skin, equipment and much more. It usually takes weeks to remove.

Photo: *Richard Hewer*

This photograph shows the original trenches dug on the site of the Knockmurton Iron Mine in 1852. The trenches exposed the upper sections of the No 13 Vein and its associated splits.

Photo: *Richard Hewer*

Cogra Moss Level, also at the Knockmurton Iron Mine. The iron ore veins at Knockmurton, Ennerdale, were worked from the middle of the 19th century. In 1872 a deep level known as Cogra Moss Adit was driven from the east and after about two years reached the first of the working veins about 1500ft in from the portal. Today the flooded adit can only be entered by descending an internal shaft from the upper workings. The photograph shows the determination that is often required to explore many of these Cumbrian iron mines. Great care is needed as it is usually impossible to see through the cold, haematite-stained water to inspect the state of the floor.

Photo: *David Bridge*

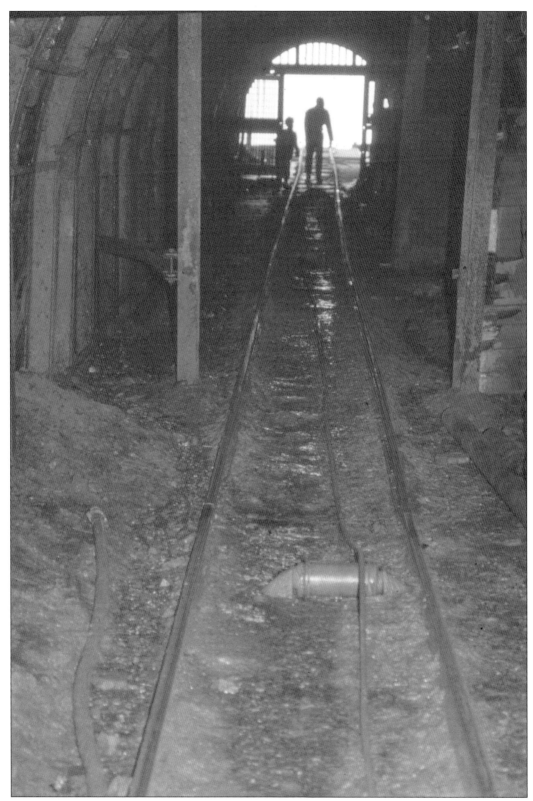

Mining at Florence Mine, Egremont, commenced in 1914, the second shaft coming into operation in 1951. It is currently owned by a partnership of miners. Due to problems with the shaft winder, an incline was driven in 1992 from the 300ft level to the surface. All traffic from the mine is now cable-hauled up the incline.

Photo: *Ken Geddes*

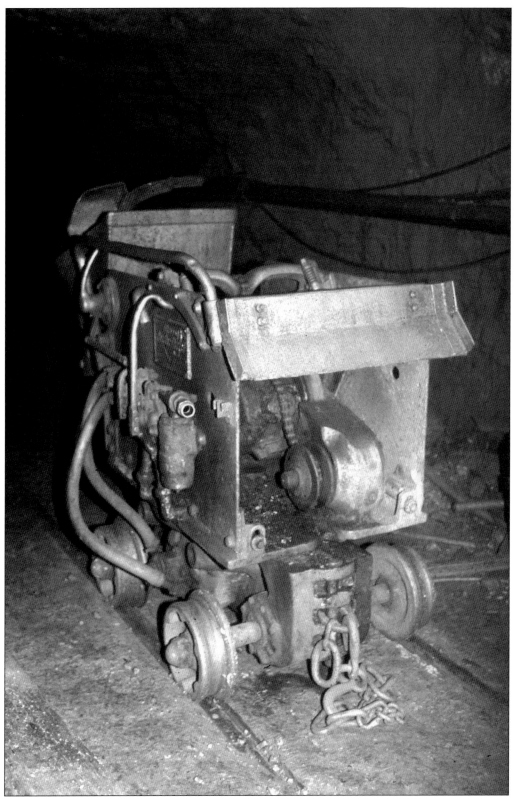

Currently workings at Florence are 30ft above the mine roadway. In this photograph a rail mounted air operated shovel ('Eimco' shovel) will make short work of loading haematite ore into rail trucks which will then be hauled up the incline.

Photo: *Ken Geddes*

In the 1970s the Florence and Ullcoats mine complex, or Beckermet Mine, extended for five miles from Calderbridge to the Uldale Valley. After 1980, the year that the British Steel Corporation closed the mine, the Egremont Mining Company continued working the upper levels largely for annealing ore and samples for the mineral trade. The slusher shown here is used for dragging the extracted ore prior to loading it into wagons.

Photo: *David Bridge*

This old bait cabin, situated high above Tilberthwaite, is possibly the only one of its kind remaining intact in the Lake District. The roof is composed of slate slabs, turf and chippings and is entire, thanks to recent remedial work carried out by CATMHS. These cabins were once a familiar sight in the Lakeland fells and provided quarrymen with a refuge from the harsh mountain weather.

Photo: *Mike Mitchell*

Walna Scar Quarries on the fells above Seathwaite, Dunnerdale, were famous for their beautifully banded slates. The bands denote the beds, or layers, of deposition, formed as the rock was laid as dust and detritus in water. The layers bear no relation to the 'bate', the plane along which all slates cleave. The bate in the slab above is denoted by the upper surface plane and runs at right angles to the beds.

Photo: *Anton C P Thomas*

Whereas slate mined on Coniston Old Man was taken from the mountain entirely by ropeway, at Honister both inclines and ropeways were used. This photograph shows the Kimberley Internal Incline, commissioned in 1938 and one of two used to carry slate from within Honister Crag to the processing sheds at Honister Hause. The incline was powered by an electric winder, situated at the incline head. When this photograph was taken the incline was out of use but is shortly to be re-commissioned.

Photo: *Jon Knowles*

In the 1980s one of the last construction jobs carried out by the McAlpine Company at Honister was the installation of roof protection in the Kimberley No 3 Level within Honister Crag. The job was never completed.

Photo: *Jon Knowles*

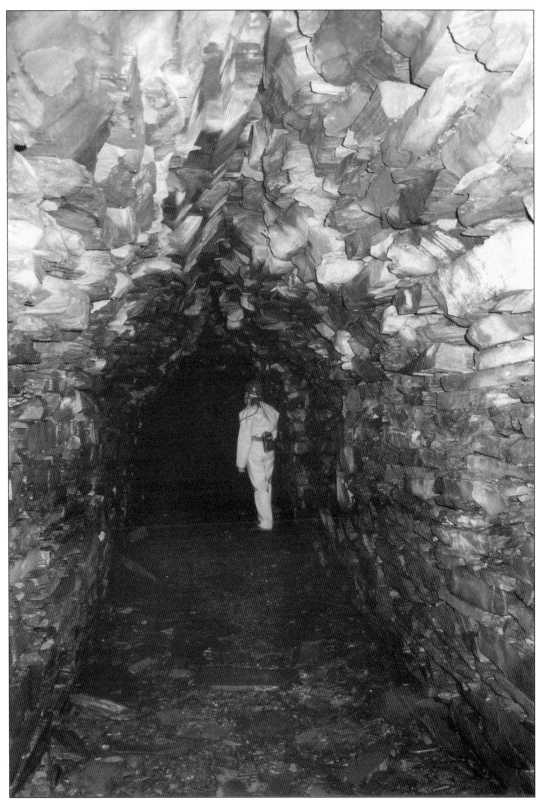

Tunnels such as this can be found in many Lakeland slate mines and are composed of walls constructed from waste slate rock which are arched over to form a safe roof. This particular one is within Yew Crag, Borrowdale, and is now completely blocked and inaccessible.

Photo: *Max Dobie*

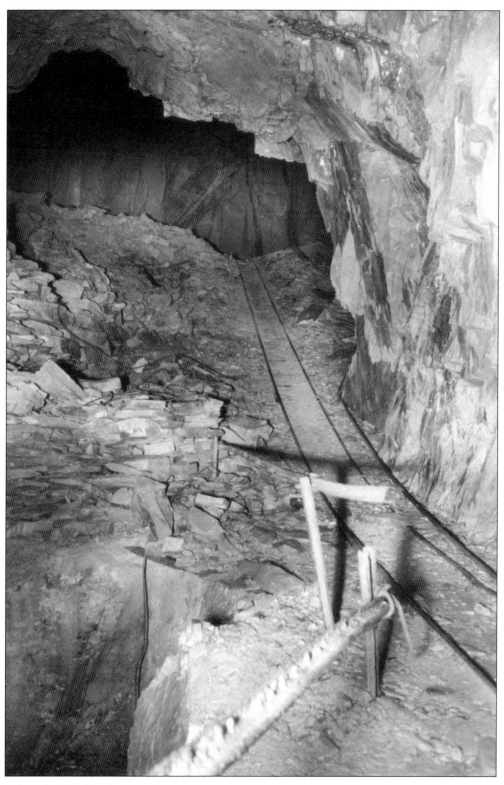

This short length of incline is situated within the Spion Kop workings on Coniston Old Man. The incline was constructed to allow slate 'clog' to be collected from the closehead at the incline head. The incline was powered by a small air winch. More recently the Moss Head workings, directly beneath Spion Kop, broke into the base from below, thus creating a sizeable underground chamber. The Old Man complex closed in 1959.

Photo: *Jon Knowles*

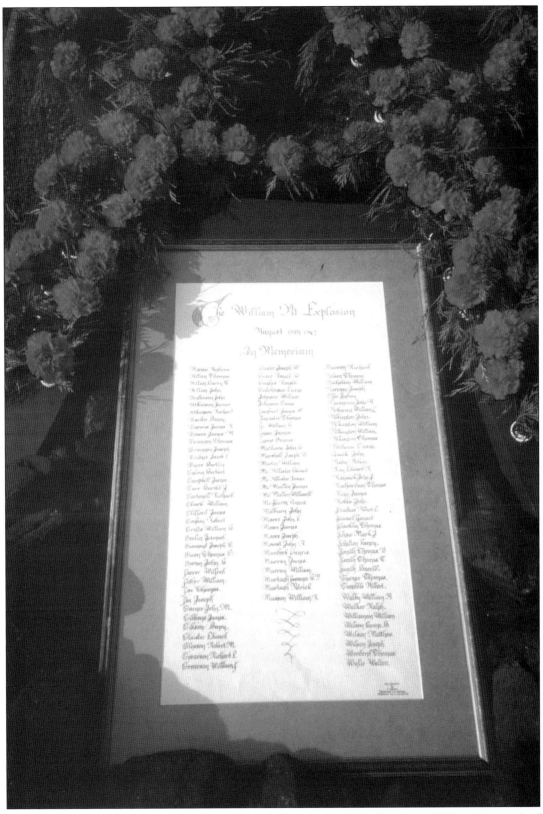

This list of the names of the 104 miners who lost their lives in the 1947 disaster at William Pit was the focal point of a memorial service held on its 50th anniversary in St Nicholas church gardens, Whitehaven.

Photo: *Ronnie Calvin*

The union banner, depicting the William Pit sunk in 1808, photographed at the commemoration service on the 27th March 1986. Some of these men had travelled a long way to be at this service, for Haig was still a part of them, as it was the centre of all our lives. The service was a simple but moving one. You could see the strain on the faces of the gathering as it progressed, but the miners of Haig would have one last go. All the colliers past and present formed up to walk proudly out of the pit yard for the last time. Carrying the last pit banner through the centre of Kells and on down the hill to the recreation ground, they were accompanied by the town band.

Photo: *Ronnie Calvin*

This photograph, taken within the Haig Engine House around 1980, shows the smaller of the two huge horizontal steam engines at Haig Pit which were the sole means of winding right up to the closure of the pit in 1986. Built by Bever and Dorling of Bradford this 5ft stroke engine has 30 inch diameter cylinders and a 14ft diameter winding drum. It was intended principally for winding men in Number 4 Shaft and has recently been restored to its former glory by volunteers of the Haig Pit Restoration Group. The engine can be seen working under compressed air in the mine museum.

Photo: *Ronnie Calvin*

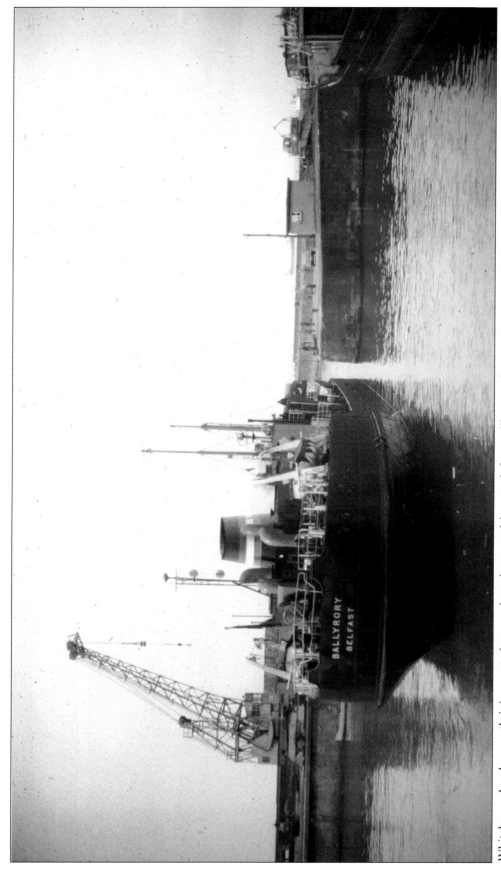

Whitehaven has been a thriving port since ancient times, and its past importance to the Cumbrian economy. Despite the fact that countless thousands of tons of iron ore and coal have been loaded from its quays, it is best remembered for the humiliating attack it suffered at the hands of Captain John Paul Jones during the American War of Independence. In recent years the town has seen a marked decline in its maritime tradition. Within the last ten years the railway sidings and the coal loading facilities have disappeared – although the sand below the harbour wall is still black with Cumbrian coal. Here the *Ballyrory*, one of the last coal boats to steam out of Whitehaven harbour laden with coal from the Haig Pit, heads out for the Irish Sea.

Photo: *Ronnie Calvin*

LAKELAND'S MINING HERITAGE – SLATE
by Alastair Cameron

Lake District slate is 450 million years old. It was formed during the Ordovician era from volcanic dust and ash. It can be split or 'cleaved' into sheets a few millimetres thick and has great resistance to climatic conditions. It is inert to virtually every form of chemical attack and is considered to be far superior to slate from other parts of Europe. It can be polished to give a beautiful finish and has become one of the most prized decorative building materials available.

Slate-working is the only aspect of mining still taking place in the Lakeland Mountains. The industry is still active and there are also signs that it may be on the increase, especially from the small scale operators who have started up in the past 30 years.

It's impossible to say with any certainty when slate-working first took place but the indications are that it could have begun in prehistoric times. Early man would have been aware of the sites where slate outcropped to the surface. He would have known of the special qualities of this rather unusual rock.

At a later period the Romans were familiar with the material and used it on their buildings. Later still, shortly after the Norman Conquest many of the monasteries and abbeys in the region were roofed with "well dressed" Lake District slate. Unfortunately, any form of documentation of these early slate workings is virtually non-existent. We can only surmise as to how the early years of the industry developed.

The first records that exist are from medieval times. There is a reference to a slate quarry being worked at Sadgill in Longsleddale in 1283 and a suggestion that some working of slate was taking place in Kirkby-in-Furness in the 1400s. It is very likely that, as with ore mining, the skills and crafts were imported from the continent to help establish the industry.

By the 1600s, with records at last available and accurate, the industry was already well developed. Workings in the Longsleddale and Kentmere areas were in steady production. So too were many of the Coniston quarries. By the early 1700s the Honister quarries were also well established. Records from this period also show that slate was being mined as well as quarried. Using techniques adapted from the ore mining industries, prospectors were driving tunnels or levels into the hillside to find richer deposits of slate deeper underground.

Future prosperity of workings would depend on three criteria: the amount of workable slate present, the quality of the slate and the ease of transporting the finished product from the working site to where it was required.

Many of the enterprises were to fail because of the last of the three. During medieval times workings were usually started at the points of outcrop, where slate was visible at the surface. As these sites were frequently in very remote places, high on the fellside above the head of the dale, slate could only be transported by pack pony. Much of the road system had not been established and unless quarrymen constructed their own access roads, the workings would not develop further than providing slate for local need.

The boom in the slate industry came about as a result of the industrial revolution. During the 1800s those locations where transport problems could be overcome developed rapidly in size, providing materials to roof the houses of the expanding communities of northern England.

In the eastern fells, Wrengill and Mosedale quarries became extensive despite their very remote locations. A cart road was constructed from the workings along the Longsleddale valley. After a lengthy journey, slate eventually arrived at the terminus of the Lancaster Canal, at Kendal, to be transported away. The nearby quarries at Kentmere also expanded and slate was carried by a similar route. Strictly speaking, the Kentmere workings were slate mines rather than quarries.

Coniston was to become a major centre for the industry. The extensive slate mines and quarries at Tilberthwaite and around Coniston Old Man had their own transport problems. Carts and sledges were used to take dressed slate from the workings down to Coniston village. Before the railway reached Coniston in 1859, slate was carted to Waterhead, taken in boats down Coniston Water to Nibthwaite, and finally by cart to the port of Greenodd.

The Walna Scar quarries above the Duddon valley became extremely productive and slate was carried directly to the coast at Angerton, near Kirkby, via Broughton Mills. The massive Kirkby quarries were reputed to be the largest in England. They also used Angerton as an outlet until the Ulverston Canal opened in 1796. Later, with the opening of the Furness Railway through Kirkby in 1846, product was removed directly by rail. An inclined tramway was built from the quarry down to the railway at Sandside.

The workings at Honister also faced major transport problems. Before 1800 most of the finished slate was taken away along a high level packhorse route known as Moses Trod, over the shoulders of some of Lakeland's highest mountains. The route ran to Wasdale Head and then on to the port of Ravenglass. Later, as Lakeland roads improved, it was possible to carry slate from the foot of Honister Crag by horse and cart. But getting the slate down from the workings on the face of Honister Crag to the Hause was another story!

During the 18th century a number of fundamental changes took place in the industry. Gunpowder was being produced locally in about 1770. By 1800 it was in sufficient supply to make it available for slate quarrying and mining. The speed at which levels could be driven and faces worked with the aid of gunpowder could not be compared with the pre-gunpowder age.

Another change took place about a hundred years later. Before about 1890 roofing slates were produced at the site of extraction in stone cabins on the quarry floor or beside the entrance to the tunnels leading into the underground mining areas. At Honister, and at a number of other locations, slate was even dressed underground. The only material to be taken from the quarry or mine was finished roofing slates. All the waste spoil was left where it was discarded. With the introduction of electrically powered saws and more robust means of transport, it was possible to carry large slate blocks away from the quarry and work them in purpose built sheds, in much improved conditions. Eventually this was to become the normal method of operation in Lakeland quarries and mines.

A further innovation was the air-powered drill, which was introduced in the early years of the 20th century. The powered drill replaced the traditional laborious hand-drilling methods for producing shot-holes, into which black-powder charges were placed. The rate at which levels could be extended and faces worked, when drills were used, was quite dramatic!

At the outbreak of the Great War many skilled slate workers were called to serve the country. It was with great reluctance that those who survived returned to the rough conditions of an industry such as slate mining. In a world of rapidly changing attitudes and standards, the working conditions in other industries became far more attractive.

By the end of the 1920s the Mosedale and Wrengill slate quarries in the Kentmere area had ceased production. So too had a number of workings at Coniston, including Walna Scar and Cove. But despite this, the industry in general was in good shape and survived the years of depression well. As some sites were closing others were expanding. At Honister slate mines a number of exploratory tunnels were driven to develop workings on new slate bands. At Torver, near Coniston, prospectors were busy on the high fells above the village. Claude Cann, son of a Cornish mining engineer, along with two companions, was trying to locate a rich area of slate. He was having very little success and was running out of money. Local opinion was sceptical. It was when his funds were virtually exhausted, and he was on the point of abandoning the project, that the level he

was driving struck the huge deposit of green slate that subsequently became the Broughton Moor Quarry.

During the 1930s and 1940s the industry began to consolidate into a relatively few areas of operation, managed by a few proprietors. Slate extraction now concentrated on the areas of Honister, Kirkstone, Langdale, Coniston and Kirkby-in-Furness. The Buttermere Green Slate Company, who owned the Honister and surrounding slate mines, also acquired workings at Tilberthwaite, near Coniston, and at Elterwater in Langdale. All these remote slate quarries and mines were subsequently closed or sold. In the 1930s the Dubbs and Rigg Head slate mines in the Honister area were also closed. This left only the Honister workings themselves and the adjacent Yew Crag slate mines still operating.

By the 1940s all the workings in the eastern part of the Lake District had closed with the exception of Petts Quarry at Kirkstone, which is still operating today.

Mandalls Slate Company worked the extensive Old Man quarries above Coniston as well as the nearby Blue Quarry, which closed during the Second World War. The Lakeland Green Slate and Stone Company operated at Moss Rigg and Hodge Close, in Tilberthwaite, a few miles north of Coniston.

In less than three years a number of major changes were to take place in Coniston. In 1962 the branch line railway to the village closed and in 1960 Mandalls ceased operation at the Old Man workings. Fortunately for the village, a year earlier, the Lakeland Green Slate and Stone Company reopened a small working at Brossen Stone high on the east side of Coniston Old Man. Brossen Stone became a very extensive slate working, despite a difficult route of transport down to the village, and survives today.

The Broughton Moor workings to the south of Coniston also expanded considerably during this period as did the Burlington Slate Quarries at Kirkby-in-Furness. Eventually these two operations, as well as Mandalls and the Lakeland Green Slate and Stone Company, merged to operate under the one name of Burlington Slate Limited.

After the Second World War there was a noticeable increase in the use of heavy machinery in the quarries: boring rigs, face shovels and heavy trucks replaced the 'old ways', and in a financially concerned environment created an economy of a scale that could not be ignored. To a great extent this was to mark the end of large scale underground slate mining. Boring rigs could rip through the rock, massive explosive charges could be laid, and huge face shovels remove slate clogs with ease. It was no longer necessary to dig tunnels to seek deep bands of slate and then mine it in underground caverns. Modern machinery and techniques could remove hundreds of feet of overburden and allow deposits of slate to be worked as open quarries.

It was inevitable that such techniques would not go unnoticed by tourists and environmental groups. From 1960 to the present day many battles have been fought in the courts and at public inquiries.

Not only were methods of operation changing but so were the markets. The building construction industry now favours light-weight synthetic materials for cladding house roofs – slate is used only in special circumstances. But new markets have opened up and there is still a world wide and expanding demand for Lakeland slate in the field of decorative cladding.

Slate is both attractive and very durable and has now been used for the cladding of many prestige buildings round the world. Its resistance to acid corrosion and other forms of attack make it very attractive to designers. New computer-aided technology has been developed and slate is cut to very tight tolerances prior to packing and shipping to destinations in the Middle East, Far East and the American Continent.

Uses are also being found for the large quantities of waste rock which accumulate on spoil tips. The development of modern and powerful crushing machines has meant that slate rock can be converted into a valuable commodity in the form of in-fill and foundation for roads and buildings, replacing limestone and gravel.

New methods of extraction are also constantly being developed. The relatively new technique of diamond-wire sawing involves cutting through rock with a diamond studded wire in a similar way to slicing cheese with a cheese-wire. The result is that far less slate is lost through damage by blasting with powder.

All this is very far removed from the days when Sammy Burns sat on his low stool cleaving slate by hand in an underground cavern at Honister at the turn of the twentieth century.

In 1985 large scale operation at the Honister slate workings ceased. In 1989 Burlington Slate closed their offices at Coniston and transferred all administration to Kirkby-in-Furness, outside the National Park. Rough blocks of slate are now transported from the various quarries to Kirkby-in-Furness for processing. The independent Kirkstone Green Slate Quarries extract slate from their site above Kirkstone Pass and transport it to Skelwith Bridge for processing.

The industry is now only a fraction of the size it was at the turn of the century. Those who walk the Lakeland fells frequently come across remains of old slate mines and quarries, a silent reminder of a once extensive industry. Over the years the workings have blended in well with the surroundings and are usually unobtrusive. Many of the valley workings have disappeared under a blanket of birch scrub.

For some time industrial archaeologists with an interest in old mine workings have studied the remains, both on the surface and underground. The lives of the quarrymen and the history of their communities are closely connected with that of the slate workings. Villages such as Coniston, Rosthwaite, Elterwater, Chapel Stile and Torver are quarrying villages which have developed over several centuries to meet the needs of the industry.

Workings in the Coniston area have been studied extensively. In the early years of this century the total workforce at the quarries on Coniston Old Man, and at Moss Rigg and Hodge Close, amounted to several hundred men and boys. Between 1870 and 1900 the workforce in the Coniston Copper Mine was declining. It was fortunate that alternative employment existed in the slate industry.

There are extensive underground workings within Coniston Old Man, from an altitude of about 1200 feet to just below the summit. The spoil tips and the former entrances are to be found on the east shoulder of the mountain. The lower entrances are now blocked but those of the upper workings, at Moss Head, have been explored in recent times. Formerly, each of these workings was separate and consisted of levels taken in from the surface for some distance into the hill until good slate 'metal' was reached. As slate was removed, a sizeable cavern was left. More extensive workings during the last sixty years have caused many of the caverns to break into each other to form enormous underground chambers. One particular void has formed at the Moss Head and Spion Kop workings. Walkers climbing Coniston Old Man by the 'tourist' route would be amazed to learn of the cavity beneath their feet.

During the 1880s slate from these high workings was taken down to Coniston village by horse-drawn sledge. In 1903 an aerial ropeway was commissioned from the workings to the road head and from then until the workings closed in 1960, this became the main means of bringing slate down. In all Coniston Old Man had five separate ropeways. The remains of them can still be seen on the mountain.

Another area, which has received the attention of industrial archaeologists, is the Honister slate workings at the head of the Borrowdale valley. The main area of extraction was inside Honister Crag and also at Yew Crag on the other side of the pass. Prior to the 1880s all 'dressed' slate was sledged by hand down the gullies and screes of Honister Crag. By 1897 an external incline had been constructed up the face of the crag and this allowed much more efficient removal of slate from the underground workings. Much of the incline remains and is considered to be one of the finest monuments to Victorian engineering in Cumbria.

In the 1920s two further underground inclines were constructed within the crag to allow larger blocks of slate to be removed for working in the newly-constructed cutting sheds at Honister Hause. From the foot of the incline, slate blocks were brought out onto the surface of the crag and carried to the Hause by aerial ropeway.

A long external incline was also constructed at Yew Crag and this remained in operation, albeit with various modifications, until the Yew Crag workings closed in 1966. Sadly, as with many such remains, the Lakeland weather took its toll and the structure of this magnificent relic started to deteriorate badly. Fortunately help was at hand and 30 years later, in 1996, the National Park Authority, with help from the Royal Commission on Historical Monuments of England and Wales, commenced restoration and stabilisation work on the structure which should allow Lakeland's oldest powered incline to be studied for many years.

There is still much more for the industrial archaeologist to interpret and preserve in the slate workings of Lakeland.

At the millennium's turn the industry is surviving well in Cumbria. The two larger manufacturers are Kirkstone and Burlington. Recently both have had major disputes with the planning authorities, which has cost them dearly. Kirkstone

operates from their major site, Petts Quarry above Kirkstone Pass and from a subsidiary 'slab' quarry at Brathay. Burlington extract 'light green' slate from Elterwater in Langdale and at Brossen Stone and Broughton Moor above Coniston. The renowned 'silver grey' slate is now being quarried again from their site at Low Brandy Crag in Coppermines Valley and dark grey sedimentary slate from their large site on Kirkby Moor.

However the most encouraging signs of prosperity come from the small manufacturers. Shortly after the end of the Second World War Jim Walker and a number of colleagues from Coniston re-opened the ancient High Fell Quarries on the lower slopes of Wetherlam. High Fell is still prosperous today, operated by Jim's son Neville and colleague George Tarr. High Fell slate is famous for its quality, colour and texture.

Lower down the slopes of Wetherlam George Tarr also re-opened Horse Crag Slate Workings in 1989. George's venture has aroused a lot of interest, not the least with the planning authorities, who see his operation as a 'blueprint' for future ventures.

Two years earlier another Coniston quarry re-opened. Sam Dugdale started to extract slate again from the ancient working of Peat Field at Hodge Close. Today Peat Field is being worked very professionally by Billy Gibson of Coniston and is producing excellent quantities of the highest quality material.

At the time of writing other potential small scale operations are being investigated and no doubt by the year 2010 the numbers will have increased further.

Probably the most exciting development to take place within the last ten years is the re-opening of the Honister slate mines. Honister had closed in 1986 and, very soon after, the processing sheds as well as the mine itself started to deteriorate. Ten years later the lease was taken up by local entrepreneur, Mark Weir of Borrowdale. Mark toiled hard to bring the workings back to life and transform them from near dereliction into a thriving operation. Today Honister is being worked by traditional methods with a major concern being to eliminate as far as possible the effect on the environment.

As well as meeting the increasing demand for Lakeland slate, these operators are keeping the ancient skills of rock-work, riving and dressing alive in Lake District villages and valleys where the pressures of tourism are increasingly having an adverse effect on the communities.

So, although the industry is surviving well at the moment, we must make sure it continues to do so. It would be a tragedy if lack of foresight and moderation by the larger quarry operators, or lack of vision and understanding by the planning authorities and the National Trust caused this traditional industry to die.

Carting silver-grey slate from the Old Man Quarries at Coniston. The track from the quarry bank on the Old Man was steep and winding, so sledges were used as in other parts of the Lakes. Not only could double the amount of slate be carted by each horse, the sledges also acted as brakes on the severe gradients. It is interesting to note that although the tracks were cobbled with slate off-cuts to provide a substantial foundation, when the quarries were in operation the tracks were covered in a superficial layer of 'rivings', the waste chips from the processing sheds, to prevent the sledges careering away and provide a smooth surface on which to run. In the far distance can be seen the miners' track descending from the copper mines at Levers Water, and the sheds at Paddy End Mine.

Photo: Ruskin Museum Archives

Hodge Close Quarry, near Tilberthwaite Gill, about 1900. Gravity was one of the main workhorses of the 19th and 20th century quarrymen. Gravity inclines became more and more elaborate as engineering skills progressed – but not only was gravity used to lower slate bogies to the processing sheds (usually situated beneath the quarries) – it was also used for raising slate from the depths. At Hodge Close, and at the Burlington Quarries at Kirkby-in-Furness, water balances were employed to great effect. The balances worked on the principle that a heavy tank of water descending on one set of guides was sufficient to raise a bogey and slate clog, to which it was attached by means of a cable and pulley system, to a predetermined height. Once off-loaded at the top of the water balance, the tank (which was then positioned at the foot) was drained and became the lighter of the two components. The weight of the empty trolley at the top was then sufficient to lift the empty tank back up the guides. At Hodge Close the slate was raised to a point midway up the quarry face, from where it was run off into a level and trammed out to day. Although the quarry is now flooded and the water balance long gone, it is still possible to walk through the level and stand at the point where the slate was off-loaded.

Photo: Ruskin Museum Archives

Hodge Close slate quarry. The date is March 1936 and Percy Rawes (left) and an assistant manoeuvre a slate tub into position as it is being lowered by the Blondin crane onto the track. The tub has been hoisted from a lower part of the quarry to the right. Tubs loaded with slate would then be taken through a tunnel to the adjoining Parrock workings and out via the Parrock Incline. Percy was foreman at the quarry for a number of years and, when he left, he took over the Cartmel Village Bakery which he ran with considerable success until he retired.

Photo: *Mrs M E Rawes*, Kendal

During the later years of operation of Hodge Close, slate from the working was taken through to the Parrock Quarry and out via the Parrock Incline.

Photo: *Mrs M E Rawes*, Kendal

Within his riving shed at Hodge Close, Fred 'Skinner' Walker dresses riven slates. The date is 1936 and Hodge Close is in full production. On the right of the photograph finished slates are neatly stacked up ready for the customer. Fred came from Coniston and both his father and grandfather held the same nickname.

Photo: *Mrs M E Rawes*, Kendal

A group of Coniston quarrymen photographed in about 1902. Not surprisingly there are some distinct likenesses between several of them and certain Coniston folk alive today.

Photo provided by *Doug Birkett*

One of the most spectacular constructions on a Lakeland mountain was the aerial ropeway or 'flight' that linked Honister Crag to the summit of Honister Hause. The ropeway was commissioned in 1926 and was finally abandoned and dismantled in 1952. The photograph, which was taken in 1978, shows the upper terminal pier of the ropeway on the face of the Crag. This is still in place today. In the distance one of the intermediate piers can be seen at Road End. This has now been dismantled. The powered driving terminal was situated at The Hause. Under normal conditions the ropeway was found to be very efficient at carrying blocks ('clogs') of slate off the Crag. In bad weather it was a different story!

Photo: *Peter Holmes*

This long powered incline raised slate from the base of the Parrock pit up to the quarry rim at Hodge Close. Parrock quarry was once an underground closehead but, in the 1890s, work started to take the roof off. This technique, known as 'open-topping' was extremely hazardous and led to the death of at least one quarryman. John Bond had only recently moved to Coniston from Cornwall to find work in the slate industry. On April 16th 1898, when working in the base of the pit, a large quantity of rock from the part-removed roof fell on him. It took his colleagues five weeks to locate and recover his body.

Photo provided by *Alastair Cameron*

A Coniston quarryman despatches a 'clog' of light green slate down the aerial flight from High Blue Quarry to the Coppermines Valley. The date is October 1938 and the following year the quarry closed and the small workforce was transferred over to the Old Man Quarries. Thirteen years earlier the Mandall Company moved into Coppermines Valley, taking over the old mine pelton wheel and compressor at the Bonsor Mill for a rent of £1 a year. They constructed a processing shed and installed an electric saw. Slate was processed there until the start of the Second World War.

Photo: *Mike Brownlee*

Within the sheds at the Coppermines Valley, a quarryman rives slate in about 1954. The slate block in the photograph had been quarried from Moss Rigg in Tilberthwaite which had been re-opened in 1948 by a group of quarrymen from Coniston.

Photo: *Mike Brownlee*

Photographs of present day small-scale slate operations at Coniston. In the top photograph Billy Gibson is using a rotary dressing machine to dress roofing slate quarried from his Peat Field Quarry. The lower photograph shows Neville Walker polishing a slab within the shed of High Fell Quarry on the slopes of Wetherlam. This particular slab became a fireplace hearth. These small scale operations are viewed by the environmentalists and National Park authorities as just the sort of local industry needed to maintain employment in the Lakeland communities.

Photo: *Alastair Cameron*

Two photographs showing some of the components of the internal inclines within Honister Crag. The photograph on the left is of the winding and braking equipment at the head of the Honister Incline. That on the right is of the carrier trolley on the Kimberley Incline. As the Honister Mine is currently being worked again for slate, all areas such as these within Honister Crag are strictly 'out of bounds'. However, the present proprietor is keen to restore both inclines and proposals are being put together with industrial archaeologists to carry out the work.

Photos: *Ian Matheson*

Beyond the head of the Kimberley Incline, within Honister Crag, the original sheaved wheel still lies in place. When the incline was commissioned in the Spring of 1934 it was powered by an electric motor and winding drum installed at the base of the incline. The cable from the drum ran around the sheaved wheel and down to the carrier trolley. In June 1957 it was decided to move the winder from the base to the top of the incline. This delicate operation was completed in a weekend and involved lifting the motor and drum up the incline on the trolley and installing it on a purpose-built concrete plinth at the top. Once installed the sheaved wheel became redundant.

Photo: *Ian Matheson*

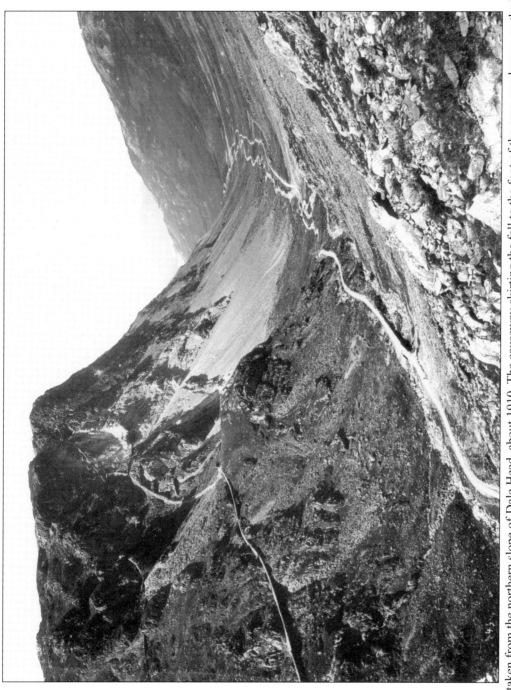

Honister Crag, taken from the northern slope of Dale Head, about 1910. The causeway skirting the fell to the foot of the crag was known as the Monkey Shelf, and was used to bring slate clogs from the incline terminus. The incline was operated by gravity, the weight of the laden trolleys descending being sufficient to haul unladen trolleys to the top. Formed in three independent sections (Ash Gill, Nag Back and Bull Gill at the lower end), slate from the Honister Vein was conveyed from the closeheads inside Fleetwith Pike, down the crag, to the processing sheds – until the incline was superseded by other methods. The lower portions have been swept away by waste tossed from the closeheads on the Kimberley Vein.

Photo: Abraham of Keswick

LAKELAND'S MINING HERITAGE – COAL
by Ronnie Calvin RM

The Cumberland coalfield extends along the coast from Whitehaven to Maryport, a distance of fourteen miles, and varies in width from four to six miles. From Maryport it continues a further twelve miles to Wigton but narrows to about two miles in width. A large area of coal has been worked under the sea bed, from Flimby down to Whitehaven. But it is in the Whitehaven area that the majority of undersea mining has taken place, with the coal being mined up to four miles out from the coast. The first coal mine in Cumbria to work the undersea coal was Saltom Pit.

There are seven principal coal seams in the Whitehaven area.

* Upper Metal Band – 3 ft 6 ins wide – 48 fathoms deep (at Wellington Pit).
* Preston Isle Yard (Burnt) – 2 ft 6 ins wide – 53 fathoms deep.
* Bannock – 6 ft wide – 74 fathoms deep.
* Main Prior – 9 ft wide – 96 fathoms deep.
* Little Main – 2 ft wide – 127 fathoms deep.
* Six Quarters – 6 ft wide – 139 fathoms deep.
* Four Feet – 2 ft 3 ins wide – 187 fathoms deep.

The dip, or direction of downward slope, of all the above seams is seaward, with a fall of approximately 1:2. The Main seam crops out near the line of the low road to St Bees, and has been worked from a very early period along the outcrop as far as Partis Pit, near Stanley Pond, Mirehouse. The Bannock Seam crops out at a correspondingly higher level. At first the coal was worked from the outcrops where the seam was exposed. Work began around 1620. The miners dug the coal, then women and girls carried it out in baskets on their backs. These early workings were known in the Whitehaven area as bearmouths, and a bearmouth roadway into the old workings still exists, just off the end of Pottery Road. This particular bearmouth was linked to Wellington Pit, then ran on to Haig Pit, William Pit and Lowca Pit. It was last reopened in March 1989 when gas was found to be penetrating into the houses on Low Road, Whitehaven. The area shaft team broke into the old bearmouth drift in order to install a ventilation chimney to draw the gas away.

One of the earliest records of coal mining in West Cumberland dates to 1560 when Sir Thomas Chaloner, lord of the manor of St Bees, in granting certain leases within the manor, reserved for himself the right to dig for coals, while at the same time granting his lessees liberty to take coals from his pits, for their own use, on the condition that they paid and laboured from time to time therein, according to the custom of the manor.

The Lowthers came on the scene in 1600 when Thomas Wybergh mortgaged the manor of St Bees to George Lowther, the eighth son of Sir Christopher Lowther. Gerard, the second son, then declared an interest. Next the eldest brother, Sir John, became the possessor and transferred his title to his second son, Christopher, who was the founder of the Whitehaven branch of the Lowther family.

Sir Christopher Lowther died in 1644 and was succeeded by his infant son,

John. On reaching manhood Sir John began to take the greatest possible personal interest in the extension of Whitehaven's trade and the development of the coal mines. Indeed, he may be truly described as the founder of the Whitehaven collieries, which were worked by the Lowthers – ably assisted by their agents, the Speddings – till August 1888, when the working pits and a large tract of submarine coal were leased to the Whitehaven Colliery Company. Thus the mines stayed in private hands till the industry was nationalised in 1947.

A major development in coal mining took place in West Cumberland about 1650, when to win new tracts of coal pits were sunk and drifts cut horizontally from the lower grounds to drain the workings. This arrangement was called the pit and adit system. The coal was originally raised by jackrolls and later by horse gins.

In 1663 Sir John Lowther drove a long level from Pow Beck near the copperas works in Ginns. This was driven in a westerly direction under Monkwray and into the Bannock Seam. The level drained an area sufficient to serve the needs of the coal trade until nearly the close of the 17th century. On the 10th of November 1715, in order to win coal from deeper levels, Lowther installed the first steam pumping engine in a Cumberland mine, at Stone Pit, Howgill, near Whitehaven. The engine, a Newcomen engine with a 17 inch cylinder, was hired for £182 per annum.

Another great feat took place in West Cumberland in 1729. The Lowthers started sinking Saltom Pit, right on the sea shore, just clear of the cliffs. The sinking of this new mine, so close to the sea and to work the coal under the sea bed, was quoted as being the most remarkable colliery enterprise of its day. When the pit had been sunk 252 feet a strong blower of gas was pricked, then piped to the pit top where it burned for many years. The agent, Mr Spedding, offered to supply the gas to the town of Whitehaven but the trustees did not take up his offer. But from an adjacent pit the gas was pumped to the laboratory of Dr William Brownridge, an eminent scientist who lived in Whitehaven, where it was used to heat his furnaces.

Throughout their history the coal mines of West Cumberland, and in particular those in the Whitehaven area, were plagued with firedamp (CH_4), and as greater depths were reached the problem of ventilation became critical. Accumulations of gas precipitated explosions which killed or maimed the colliers and seriously damaged the underground workings. One of the earliest of these explosions happened at Priestgill Colliery, in 1682, killing one miner and injuring six more. To the employer, the damage done to the mines was more important than the loss of life.

New methods of lighting and ventilation were tried. One of the most important of the early inventions was the Spedding steel mill, the first attempt to produce a safe means of lighting in an atmosphere containing firedamp. This new device was merely a steel disc fixed to a small cogwheel and geared to a larger wheel. When the handle was turned a piece of flint was held against the disc, creating a stream of sparks which enabled the miners to see to work.

The use of the Spedding steel mills spread throughout the north of England. They were used till the introduction of the Davy lamp in 1819. A fine example of a steel mill is on display in Whitehaven Museum.

But still the terrible carnage to women, boys, girls and colliers, took place on a regular basis. The rescue of the miners and the fighting of the underground fires were left to the miners and agents. The owners played a very small part in rescue, their main concern being the damage and how much money they would lose. Early rescue workers were untrained; just ordinary workmen willing to give their lives, sometimes in vain attempts to rescue trapped workmates. As methods progressed a few specially trained workmen were, from time to time, called on to rescue miners, fight underground fires and recover bodies.

These trained men gave a very valuable service but it was not until the 20th century that the first fully trained West Cumberland rescue team was set up at Brigham.

The first Coal Mines Act was introduced in 1842, forbidding the employment of women underground. On the 10th of August 1850 the Act for the inspection of coal mines received the royal assent. It provided for the appointment of inspectors and the official registration of all mine accidents. These first inspectors had very little power and no qualifications. The penalties for mine owners who breached the regulations under the 1855 Act was a fine of £5 with an additional fine of £1 per day until the law was complied with. Offending colliers, however, might be imprisoned for up to three months.

In 1851 the Royal School of Mines was set up to train the inspectors, but it was not until 1872 that real progress was made. The Act made it compulsory for all mine managers to pass a Government

examination of competence – this is now called the 1st Class Ticket.

The first mines inspector for Cumberland was Matthis Dunn, who was appointed in November 1850. He also had to inspect collieries in Northumberland, Durham and Scotland – which did not leave much time to inspect the Cumberland mines. The last resident inspector was Mr Stephen, a gentleman who was always willing to give help and advice on all aspects of mine safety. After he left in 1983 the county's mines were covered by visiting inspectors, Mr Vincent and Mr Armstrong, the latter being a former resident inspector

who was familiar with the gas and geological problems of the coalfield.

Wooden props were the main means of supporting coal workings but at the pit bottoms – and main haulage roads and junctions – brick walls were built and roofed in timber, second-hand steel and old tramlines. The timbers used in the Whitehaven mines of 1750 were imported from Norway by Sir James Lowther. There was a large number of these 'Noraways', as they were called locally, in the old Wellington workings, up by Saltom Drift off Haig No 5 coal road. Some of these timbers are still supporting the old workings, and predate Haig's sinking (1911). Some of the large 24 inch square head setts up at the old junctions were still as good as the day they were set. And if you were lucky enough to be near repair work in some of these old places, the off cuts made great kindling wood for the fire.

Wood was also used for brake blocks on winders and haulages. The railway poplar trees (poplus and Eurasnericana regenerata) from the Penrith area, were planted when the railway authorities altered the route of the London to Glasgow line in the 1880s. The requirement was that each butt had to be at least 30 inches through and more than 10 feet in length, clear of branching. The last tree from this local source was supplied to the Cumbrian colliers in 1979 by Mr John Hird, the timber merchant. A local landowner has planted more in case they are required at some time in the future.

Although there is a wealth of information to be found on the Alston area, and specifically on the lead mining industry, there is a paucity of material about coal mining. The most comprehensive source is the *Victoria County History*, but even there the bias is towards the West Cumberland coalfields rather than East Cumberland.

According to the *Victoria County History* the first record of an early attempt to prove coal in East Cumberland is in the books of the Newcastle Corporation wherein it is stated that in 1552 coal was bored for in Greenside Rigg in the parish of Farlam. However, Bouch claims, in *Prelates and People of the Lake Counties*, that the Dacre family worked the mines at Tindale Fell before 1485.

The earliest collieries were found mainly in the valleys of the Black, Hartley and Haining burns, at Thirwell, Tarnhouse Colliery (Tindale Fell), Talkin and Brampton, and during the 19th century at Croglin, Blenkinsop and Lambley in Northumberland. Harris says, in *Cumberland and Westmorland Transactions 1974*, that the Carlisle Papers (at the Department of Palaeography and Diplomatic of the University of Durham) contain a wealth of information about the mining history of East Cumberland. They refer particularly to output, royalties and the rise and decline of collieries, but also include information about colliery farms, small-holdings and the character of settlements generally within the mining areas.

With regard to Alston, the first known source appears to be M Jars in 1765, who described in his book *Voyages Metallurgiques the Crow Coal in the mountains of Alston Moor* as being unfit for the forge, but excellent for burning lime. Jollies' *Directory* from 1811 mentions that Alston produces lead ore and coal, but gives no details. Parson and White's *Directory* from 1829 describes the Crow Coal as "containing a large portion of pyrites, burns very slowly, but is intensely hot, with very little flame, and emits a strong smell of sulphur. It is found in thin seams near the surface and is used by the miners, who mix it with clay, and make it up into balls for the fire". Subsequent directories merely repeat this information.

The major area of mining activity (at least as documented) appears to have been Tindale Fell where there were many pits. In 1801 Tarnhouse, on Tindale Fell, and Talkin Collieries, produced 197,015 loads of coal.

The output rose to 278,615 loads in 1810. The drifts then at work were William, Morpeth, Fox, George and Henry.

From early times coal had been worked at other places from the carboniferous limestone series along the Pennine range, but apparently it was mainly used for lime burning. The most important area of such mining was said to have been at Croglin. When the manor of Croglin was purchased by Charles, Duke of Somerset, in 1738, it included a colliery which was in continuous operation till 1864.

There were also early coal workings at Hartside and Renwick in the Crossfell range, the earliest reference being in the account book of Lady Anne Clifford, 1665.

Payed for Pitt Colls for my Howfs heare att Brougham Castle – Payed the 2: Day [May 1665] to John Unthank of Culgart and others for 50 loads of Pittcoals for my house here at Broughm Castle brought from Hartshead in Cumberland at 1s per load two pounds and ten shillinges.

In 1900 the *Victoria County History* lists forty-three collieries in Cumberland, three of which were at Alston and one at Nenthead. These were:
* Alston Drift Colliery, owned by
  W Benson, with fifteen employees.
* Guttergill Colliery, owned by Vieille Montagne Zinc Co, with seven employees.
* Rock Hill Colliery, the Alston and Nentforce Limestone Quarry Co, with six employees.
* Dowgang Colliery, Vieille Montagne Co, seven employees.

In 1905 these firms were the only producers of coal at Alston and did not employ more than forty persons underground in the aggregate. The three firms were all working the little limestone coal which in the Alston district is found in two distinct seams, twenty feet apart, the upper being about twenty inches thick and the lower twelve inches thick.

The total number employed in 1900 in the collieries was 8,646, the great majority of whom were in the West Cumberland coalfields. When put in this context the Alston collieries must be seen as very small.

The Cumbria Sites and Monuments Record shows mine-related sites at Blagill (NY7347), Hesleywell (NY7547), Rotherhope Fell (NY7142), Nenthead (NY7844), Garrigill (NY7544), Crossgill (NY7441), and Middle Fell (NY7388, NY7443). This information has been picked up from 1st edition Ordnance Survey maps and contains no details of the various sites. However, according to R Fairburn, the Nenthead levels which were driven to exploit the Coalcleugh coal were worked by a small group of miners from 1840 to 1940 (SMR5911).

Aside from the records at Durham University, it may well be that company records for Vieille Montagne Co and the others mentioned above are in existence and could prove useful. Also, the NCB may have an archive or early material.

Coal has also been worked on a small scale in the Caldbeck, Shap and Stainmoor areas. At Caldbeck, the little limestone coal crops out on the southern flanks of Warnfell Fell, and numerous shafts indicate that the seam has been extensively worked. Its thickness is said to vary between 1 foot and 2½ feet. A lot of this coal would have been used for lime burning.

T Eastwood makes reference to a plan dated 1847 showing workings in the little limestone coal, north-east of the Denton fault belt, and the waterwheel and steam engine pits of Denton Holme Colliery, situated near Sebergham church. This coal was said to have been 20 inches thick at a depth of 160 feet in the waterwheel shaft.

Coal was also worked in the limestone near Paddigill. Again this was thin coals associated with the limestone. If you study the place names around Sebergham you will see that lime burning was carried out in this area, Kiln Gate and Lime Kiln Nook, for example. There are still a lot of old lime kilns marked on the Ordnance Survey maps.

Coal was worked on a small scale between Sleagill and Reagill, near Shap. To this day there are two fields called Pit Hills. It was also worked on a small scale at many localities in the lower carboniferous series at Borrowdale, Stainmoor, and in the westphalian Argill coalfield. Mining on Stainmoor dates from an early period, as the account book of Lady Anne Clifford illustrates:

Payed for Stainmor pitt coals for my Howfs heare at Brough Castle in Westmorland – Payd the 22nd Day [December 1665] to Robt Barret for 120 loads of Pitt Coals for my houfe hear att Brough Castle in Westmorland at 10d a load, ffive pounds.

Coal was worked by adits on the north bank of Argill Beck, where it was said to have been nearly 4 feet thick. A trial pit was sunk in 1946 in Argill Beck and two feet of coal, overlain by siltstone, was proved. The last small coal working in this area was an adit, now collapsed, where coal up to 7 feet thick was said to have been worked. Mining ceased in 1946.

Postscript

Since I wrote my notes on Coal Mining in 1991, two very important events have taken place to help us remember all the men, women and children who have lost their lives down the West Cumberland coal mines, a total number of 1,237.

The first event was on 16th August 1997, when the town's people turned out in force for a service in St Nicholas Gardens to pay tribute to the 104 miners who lost their lives 50 years previously in William Pit.

This was a simple but moving occasion carried out with great dignity; the local school children placing lighted candles into a model of the Pit Top 'shere' wheel as each miner's name was called out. Then the people walked behind the Cumberland Miner's Banner, through the town to William Pit where the final part of the service was carried out by the Bishop of Carlisle.

The second event took place the following year on the same date, the 16th August, marking the 51 years that have elapsed since William Pit took 104 miner's lives. The Whitehaven Memorial Committee, whose hard work and dedication made the first memorial service possible, then set to work to raise £18,000 for a permanent memorial to all who had lost their lives in our pits.

The local people put their hands into their pockets and purses and Copeland Borough Council pledged them the £18,000 until it was raised.

This sum and more was raised so that on 16th August 1998, on a bright and sunny day (just like it was 51 years ago when the William Pit disaster occurred) the local people gathered in St Nicholas Church Gardens for the unveiling of a beautiful pebble mosaic dedicated to all those killed in Whitehaven coal mines from 1597 to 1986.

Again the people walked behind the pit banner over the old wagon road to William Pit, where there was an equally poignant dedication of a black granite memorial stone listing the thirteen explosions which took place there.

So ended a sad day. These are sad occasions but the tragedies and sacrifices made in our mines must never be forgotten.

Natural 'roundheads' – the local term for slates dressed in the traditional fashion – high in the Lakeland fells. Here the slate outcrops on the surface and has burst, either through the action of severe frost or by the hand of 19th century man, to fall in perfectly cleaved slabs. The 'bate', the cleavage inherent in all slates, can be discerned edge on, running at a steep angle through the 'growing' rock.

Photo: *Peter Fleming*

Within the level of a Coniston slate mine strange ice formations have been created. Extremely cold air drawn into the mine freezes water dripping from the level roof.

Photo: *Mike Mitchell*

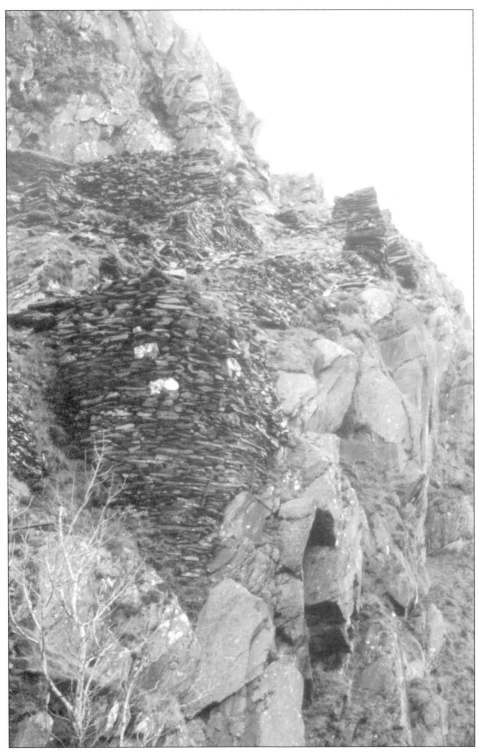

The external incline which runs up the face of Honister Crag is justly considered to be one of the most spectacular Victorian structures in Cumbria. Much of the stonework supporting the incline railway was keyed into ledges cut into the rock face and held there with iron pins. As well as the rail trucks, quarrymen also used the incline to get to and from their work places. It was from the top of walled buttresses such as these that waste rock was tipped over the edge to cascade down the rock face and scree below. Understandably few rock climbing routes were ever attempted on Honister Crag.

Photo: *Mike Mitchell*

Two photographs of rail equipment within the Honister Slate Workings taken during the period that Bernard Moore operated the mine. The electric loco was removed when the mine closed but the side tipping truck remained. Sadly it was vandalised during the period of time that the mine was not being worked.

Photo: *Ian Matheson*

To the north east of Alston productive coal measures have been worked successfully in private drift mines. The first photograph here shows the main road in Clargill Colliery which extends for about a mile into the fellside. The second photograph shows the working of a face of a narrow seam in Clargill.

Photo: *Ronnie Calvin*

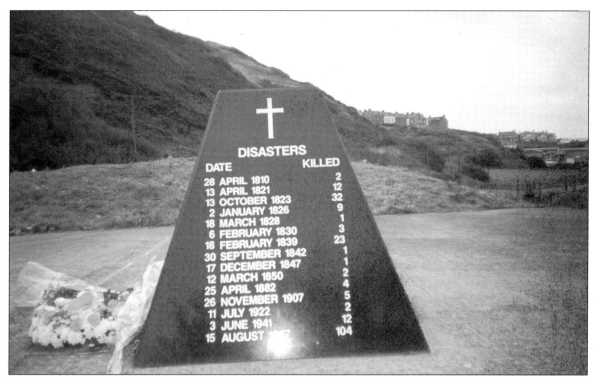

DISASTERS	
DATE	KILLED
28 APRIL 1810	2
13 APRIL 1821	12
13 OCTOBER 1823	32
2 JANUARY 1826	9
18 MARCH 1828	1
6 FEBRUARY 1830	3
18 FEBRUARY 1839	23
30 SEPTEMBER 1842	1
17 DECEMBER 1847	1
12 MARCH 1850	2
25 APRIL 1882	4
26 NOVEMBER 1907	5
11 JULY 1922	2
3 JUNE 1941	12
15 AUGUST 1947	104

Before it closed in 1955 William Pit at Whitehaven had claimed the lives of over 200 workers, mostly through gas explosions. The greatest disaster occurred on 14th August 1947 in the main haulage road some two and a half miles out under the sea when 107 men were trapped behind heavy falls. Only three of those men escaped alive. This memorial to all who lost their lives in William Pit over the years, seen here 51 years to the day after the 1947 disaster, stands at the wind-swept site of the pit along Whitehaven's north shore.

Photos: *Ronnie Calvin*

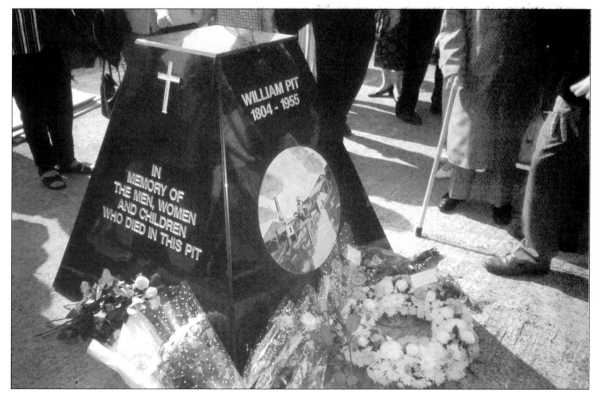

WILLIAM PIT
1804 - 1955

IN MEMORY OF THE MEN, WOMEN AND CHILDREN WHO DIED IN THIS PIT

Pit deputy Ronnie Calvin, Davy lamp on his belt, inspecting a mono pump at Rigg's pump lodge, down in the depths of the Haig Pit. The Haig Pit was considered to be a dry mine, despite the fact that the main coal faces were several miles out under the Irish Sea.

A confluence of tram lines can be seen here at the entrance to South Side off No 5 Coal Road in Haig Pit.

Photos: *Ronnie Calvin*

Testing for gas with a Davy lamp prior to entering Quinn's Drift during salvage work in the Upper Metal Band. Note the ventilation doors and the rope haulage.

Photo: *Ronnie Calvin*

Coppermines Valley, as the name implies, was the centre of Coniston's mining industry. In the foreground are the cottages of Irish Row, built for immigrant miners escaping the Irish famines and land clearances of the 19th century. In the centre of the picture are the Bonsor dressing floors, the focal point of activity. The white building in the centre was once the mine office – now it belongs to the Youth Hostel Association. The cottage to the right was the manager's house and stable – now it is a mountaineering hut. To the right, Red Dell, scene of exploitation on the Bonsor Vein, ascends to the crags, while to the left the mine track winds around Kernal Crag to Grey Crag, Paddy End Mine and the Elizabethan workings above Levers Water.

Photo: *Peter Fleming*

Copper has been mined at Scope End on the NW spur of Hindscarth since early times. This view shows open works developed in the 16th century by the German miners brought over by the Company of Mines Royal who named the mine Gottesgab ('God's Gift' since corrupted to 'Goldscope'). When the hand-chiselled copper mine adit was widened and extended in Victorian times a rich vein of lead was discovered which produced 5000 tons of ore yielding 22,000 ounces of silver.

Photo: *David Bridge*

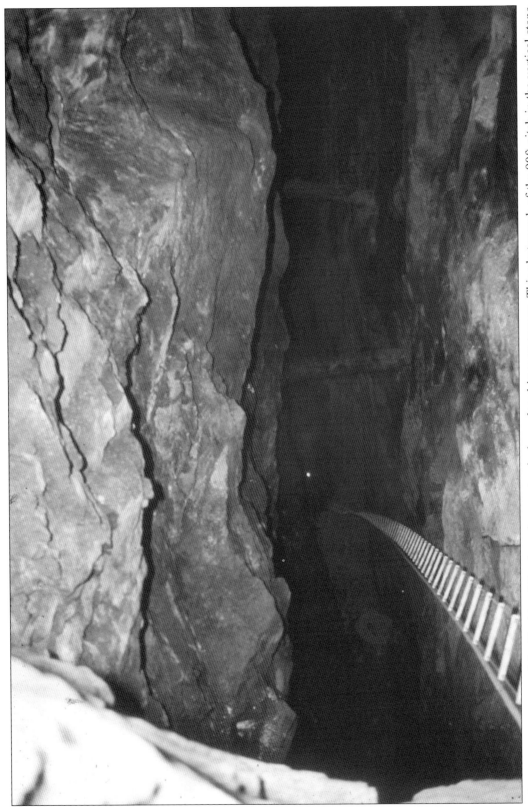

The great open stopes of the Coniston Mine have been extensively explored in recent years. This photograph of the 90ft pitch in the vertical stope below Arete Chamber in the Paddy End area of the mine shows the route that was once part of the 'through trip' that explorers established from Levers Water to Hospital Level at Paddy End. After a major underground collapse in 1996 the route became blocked.

Photo: *Mike Mitchell*

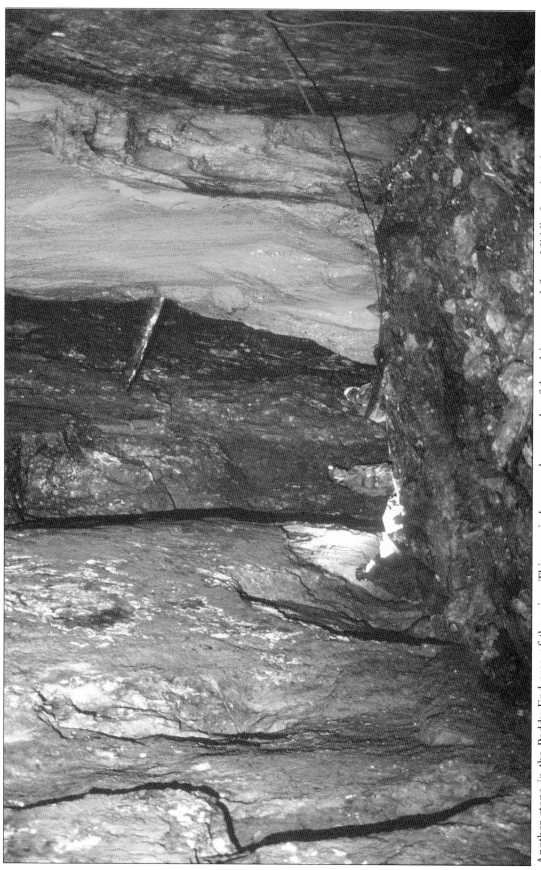

Another stope in the Paddy End area of the mine. This one is large and very colourful and is accessed from Middle Level. A large amount of secondary mineralisation has taken place in this area.

Photo: *Mike Mitchell*

The photograph of Angela Wilson of Cumbria Amenity Trust was taken on 27th November 1988 during the first exploration of the upper reaches of the Bellman Hole workings high above Top Level in the Coniston Copper Mines. The shaft she is crossing was later descended and was found to connect with the Top Level system below.

Photo: *Peter Fleming*

The photograph of Peter Fleming was taken within the inner reaches of Middle Level, Coniston Copper Mines, showing an ore hopper coming down from the Top Level workings with an abundant cover of secondary copper deposits of blue and green all round.

Photo: *Jef Wilkinson*

High on the slopes of Wetherlam close to the Wetherlam Mine are the remains of the gearing and drive mechanism of a horse gin, virtually intact. This gin was manufactured by John Fell & Co of Wolverhampton in about 1900 and installed by the operators of the Wetherlam Mine, Thomas Warsop and Charles Day.

Photos: *Mike Mitchell* and *Peter Fleming*

Details of a well-preserved barrow wheel discovered in the Paddy End section of the Coniston Coppermine. Wheelbarrows were made on site and there were many different patterns. The wheels were usually made of iron but this one was made from a solid piece of wood, and shod with an iron rim by the mine smith.

Photo: *Ian Matheson*

A view up the rise to Woodends Level below Levers Water in the Coniston Coppermines. Copper salts cover the rock walls almost entirely.

Photo: *Mike Mitchell*

The oak barrier or 'plug' which seals a tunnel beneath Levers Water was, for many years, thought to be only a local legend, until it was discovered by a team of industrial archaeologists in 1987. The plug was thought to have been installed under the instructions of John Barratt in 1844 (a year of severe drought) to allow the level of the tarn to be raised. In 1999 the North West Water Authority considered their reservoir was at risk and sealed the access tunnel with concrete.

Photo: *Peter Fleming*

From Coniston Coppermines Valley the Bonsor Vein struck in an easterly direction under the flank of Wetherlam. This photograph shows the abundant traces of iron which occurred in Deep Level in this area and also the remains of a wooded gunpowder barrel. It is recorded that several tons of lead ore and also green-slate were recovered from this part of the mine in the 1890s.

Photo: *Peter Fleming*

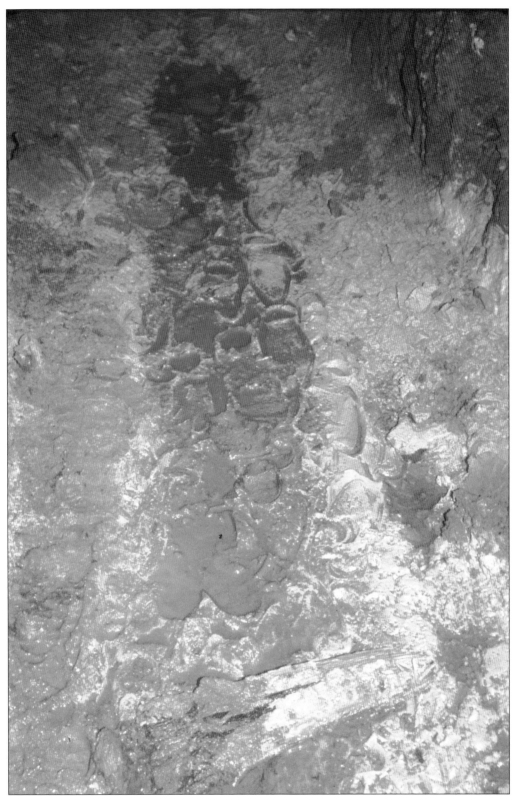

In 1984 a portion of the Paddy End area of Coniston Coppermines, known as Levers Water Mine, was re-opened and drained of water. On exploring the mine, industrial archaeologists discovered these perfectly preserved clog prints in the mud, left by the last miners approximately 100 years ago.

Photo: *Mike Mitchell*

In 1982 this spectacular formation was discovered in an inaccessible part of the Coniston Coppermines, in an extension of Taylor's Level. The deposits have been created by secondary mineralisation since the mine was closed. It is known as 'The Blue Cascade'.

Photo: *Mike Mitchell*

One of the many colourful areas of Levers Water Mine at Coniston where minerals have been leached out by the action of water and become deposited during the 100 years since the closure of the mine.

Photo: *Mike Mitchell*

Sections of the wooden pumping rods are still in place in the Old Engine Shaft of the Coniston Coppermines. This photograph shows part of the rods and the 'catch-wing' (a restraining device) in the shaft.

Photo: *Max Dobie*

A further view of the pump rods within the Old Engine Shaft. The rods were operated by the 'big wheel', a notable feature on the fell side above the Coppermines Valley and were connected to the pumps in the lowest part of the mine. The timber to make these rods was specially imported from Canada and made up a total length of over 1300ft.

Photo: *Mike Mitchell*

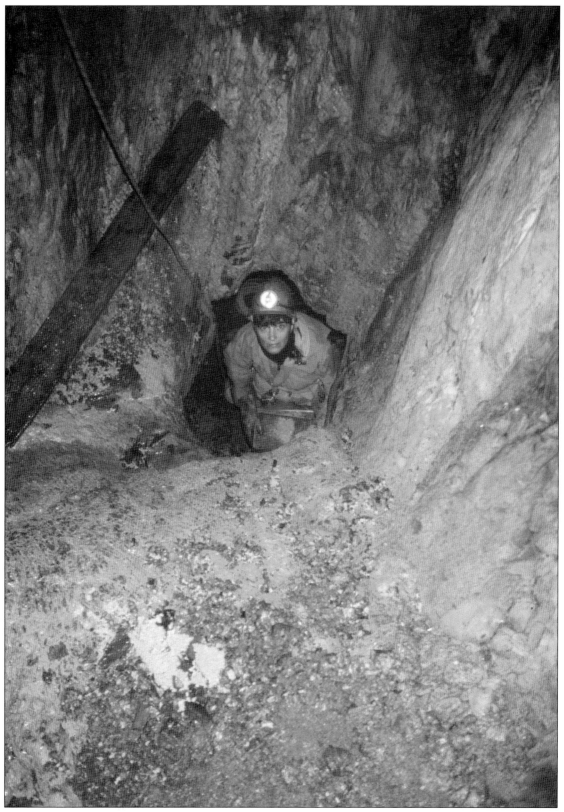

Copper sulphates and other colourful copper minerals known as 'post mine supergenes' are deposited on the walls of this shaft by water draining from Woodend's Level in the upper part of the Paddy End workings.

Photo: *David Bridge*

LAKELAND'S MINING HERITAGE – COPPER

by Peter Fleming

In the context of world wide technological history, the 'copper age' began in Mesopotamia as long ago as the 7th millennium BC, when copper in its native form was discovered to be malleable and durable. It could be shaped when beaten with stone hammers.

The earliest copper artefacts ever found were beads, pins and awls. Two thousand years were to elapse before this craft reached south eastern Europe in 5000 BC. By this time simple food vessels formed from beaten copper sheets were in use and axe heads and spear heads were being produced.

The word copper comes from the Latin 'cyprium' meaning 'ore of Cyprus'. It is believed that copper smelting was developed as early as 6000 BC in Iran. In Crete, small pieces of azurite have been discovered in a habitation layer dated to the same period. The ladies of Ancient Egypt used powdered malachite in their make-up.

The first actual record of copper mining, again in Mesopotamia, is dated to 3500 BC. Across the other side of the world, copper artefacts have been discovered in Peruvian tombs of 2000 BC. These facts support the long held theory that the Middle Eastern and South American cultures were centuries ahead of the European Stone Age. Recent discoveries in certain copper mines in North Wales look like proving this belief to be incorrect. In 1988, stone tools, bones and traces of fire-setting were found in underground workings on Great Ormes Head, at Parys Mountain and Cwmystwyth Mine. From charcoal taken from these sites, the British Museum has carried out carbon dating tests which suggest that the workings on Great Ormes Head could date from between 1000 BC and 1800 BC. It seems this part of history may have to be revised.

So copper in its native form was the first metal used by man. Later oxidised zones of copper deposits must have attracted attention where they came to surface – the 'outcrop' as it is known, with blue and green carbonates (azurite and malachite) being quite obvious. These two minerals have been used from even earlier times to make jewellery and for painting. To obtain metallic copper from these ores was a simple matter of applying heat with wood or charcoal using a primitive bellows. After the miners had exploited the outcrops, they were naturally led to work the cupriferous lodes in depth. Instead of decomposed ore altered by the weathering action of air and percolating rain water, they met with an unaltered substance of shiny brassy yellow colour and high specific gravity, called yellow copper pyrites (chalcopyrite). It is also known as yellow sulphide of copper as its consistency is a combination of copper and sulphur with an equal portion of iron, approximately 33% of each. The techniques of copper smelting reached Britain by the beginning of the second millennium BC. To produce metal from copper pyrites was not straightforward. How did man learn to smelt these copper sulphides and how did the ancient copper smiths become aware that these ores must be roasted in contact with air before smelting, in order to remove the sulphur content? A reasonable theory put forward is that potters using copper minerals to produce coloured glazes hit upon the technique by accident. Doubtless the process was established after a long period of experiment.

There is no evidence, either scientific or documentary, to prove that mining took place in the Lake District prior to the early part of the thirteenth century when, as recorded in the close rolls of Henry III, Goldscope Mine at Newlands near Keswick was being worked for copper. It would be reasonable to think however that the Romans could have been active in the Caldbeck Fells and very likely in the Coniston Fells as well.

Consider again for a moment the recent discoveries mentioned previously in North Wales and bear in mind that two major Neolithic stone axe working sites are to be found in central Lakeland on the Langdale Pikes and on the Scafell Range. It may yet be proved that the early 'entrepreneurs' using their stone tools worked the copper veins where they would so obviously outcrop on the surface at that time.

The copper mines of the Lake District are to be found almost entirely in the Skiddaw slates. One notable exception is the Coniston Copper Mines, which lie within a volcanic area of hard rhyolite. The mineral deposits found within both these areas occur in the faults and fissures caused, it is believed, by upward pressures of an underlying granite mass. These cracks were filled by circulating, mineral bearing, solutions (which may have been either hot or cold) during the carboniferous period. Owing to the almost vertical inclination of these faults, the mines developed on the richer ore bearing ones went very deep – 700 ft at Goldscope and over 1600 ft at Coniston. These sorts of depths presented considerable problems to the miners of over one hundred years ago. By far the most common copper ore mined in the Lake District has been the brass-yellow chalcopyrite (a sulphide). Bornite or peacock ore, which displays beautiful variegated colours, is also a sulphide and has been found at the Dalehead, Goldscope and Coniston mines in recent years.

The two carbonates, malachite and azurite (green and blue respectively), occur in the oxidised zones near to the surface and were both exploited. Each contains around 55% copper. Hydrous silicate of copper 'chrysocolla' has been found, mainly in the Caldbeck Mining field and to a lesser extent at Coniston, and this is an attractive turquoise blue mineral.

It is generally accepted that the mining of copper in Lakeland did not start in any significant way until the arrival of the mining experts from Germany in 1563. Queen Elizabeth I granted an indenture on the 10th December 1564 to Thomas Thirland, their English mining agent and his German protégé Daniel Höchstetter, permitting them to dig for ores throughout the land. The richest copper mine known at that time in Lakeland was named by the Germans 'Gottesgab' (God's Gift), which became corrupted into 'Goldscope', the name it is known by today. They started there at Easter 1556, working on a vein up to 9 ft thick. By 1568 the Company of Mines Royal had been formed. The mines of the Caldbeck Fells received a first mention in their accounts for this year.

The Company had an ingenious way of paying their miners. Everything they used, from candles to clothing and food, was deducted from their earnings automatically, so that they avoided the difficulties of trading locally with money they did not understand. They tended to be rather independent and isolated. Initially most of them lived on Vicar's Island in

Derwent Water, which they purchased for £60 in 1569, but gradually they began to integrate with the local people. Many marriages were recorded between the girls of Keswick and the miners, and their Germanic names can still be traced today, for example, Moser, Parker and Senogles, etc.

The Company spent lavishly in the locality of Keswick, chiefly on the development of the copper and lead mining areas. Smelt mills were erected to treat the ore and a whole network of packhorse trails was set up to transport the ores and the charcoal to smelt them. To produce the charcoal, Borrowdale, along with other valleys, was denuded of its trees. So good were the terms of payment to such a previously impoverished district, that prosperity was brought to many, and lucrative jobs provided for many more, whose previous existence had been limited to scraping a living from fell farming or simple rural trades.

The *Keswick Journal* for 1659 contains reference to the Germans working a copper mine on the west shore of Buttermere and this can still be traced today. In the Newlands Valley, other copper mines worked at this time included Dalehead, Castlenook and the nearby Longwork and St Thomas' Work. Over the ridge of Maiden Moor to the east in Borrowdale two copper veins had not escaped the notice of the Mines Royal. These were the Manesty Vein, otherwise known as the Saltwell Mine, and the other the Copperplate Vein not far from Grange in Borrowdale. The largest

production area for copper other than Goldscope would undoubtedly be in the Caldbeck Fells. Some of the larger mines were Roughton Gill Mine, Mexico Mine, Silver Gill Mine and Red Gill Mine. The latter is famous for its rare, deep azure blue crystals of linarite, a sulphate of copper and lead, specimens of which can be seen in the Natural History Museum. In addition to copper, considerable tonnages of lead were

extracted from these mines. It was some time after 1590 that the Company of Mines Royal discovered, or rediscovered, some of the numerous and extensive copper veins at Coniston. Traces of their work can still be seen in the lower and upper parts of Red Dell in the form of hand driven 'coffin' shaped levels. The lower one, known as Cobblers Level, was probably the first cross cut driven into the rich Bonsor Vein. It was completed in 1624. The higher one was driven to work a small, isolated vein known as 'God's Blessing'. This was started in 1620. Both these tunnels have, at a later date, been widened with explosives to accommodate wheelbarrows. The German miners had also been working on the veins outcropping at Levers Water. In a Commission report dated 1602 three mines were named. One, 'Sebastian' was then wrought 24 ft deep from the surface. The other two were named St Lenard and St William.

In January 1617 a hand cut drainage adit was started to draw water from the deepening Sebastian work. Four and a half years later, on the 20th June 1620, it was completed after driving 40 fathoms. At this time it would be a most expensive and laborious undertaking.

The opening up of Coniston mines came too late to save the Company of The Mines Royal. The parent company, Haug Laugnaure & Co, the Augsberg firm who financed the mining operations in the Lake District, were heavily in debt and had already handed over their interests to the English shareholders and those of the Germans who had chosen to remain here. This included the Höchstetter family, who, it is recorded, put forward the idea of building a smelter at Coniston to avoid the long packhorse trail to the Keswick smelters with the ore. This idea was never pursued until the end of the nineteenth century.

Mining continued until the outbreak of civil war in 1642. Little seems to have been done during the rest of the seventeenth century, but Greenburn Mine, situated in the valley of that name in Little Langdale, appears as a producer of copper for the first time. It is also interesting to note that gunpowder was introduced in the Coniston mines in 1694. Goldscope was going through a lean period with only sporadic activity. The longest period of continuous work was between 1680 and 1690. Mining in the Caldbeck Fells had declined before the outbreak of the Civil War and was reported as "left and given over".

Reasons were various. Some blamed the loss on the death of the first generations of German artisans, and their descendants not possessing the same skills, but more significant in fact was the scarcity of timber to produce charcoal. The land had been stripped, and the visual impact must have been considerable. It took half an acre of trees to provide the charcoal for each ton of ore smelted. It was even planned to import timber from Ireland. Commonwealth troops were alleged to have destroyed the Keswick smelters and associated works. They were left "ruinated and spoyled".

This state of affairs lasted throughout the first half of the eighteenth century despite numerous leases having been taken out with landowners, both at Coniston and Caldbeck. However, in 1758 the Macclesfield Copper Company was formed under the directorship of one Mr Charles Roe. This Company was to spend the next thirty-seven years working on the rich Bonsor Vein at Coniston, taking it down below the old German workings which were in excess of 150 feet below the surface. Charles Roe built a water wheel to drive a pump and raise ore up a narrow and constricted shaft within the vein itself. It is still possible today to see the deep grooves cut into the foot wall of the shaft, where the heavy chains constantly rubbed. This was the Bonsor East Shaft. During the first ten years of operation the output averaged one hundred tons of finished copper per year. Work was also going on at Paddy End and Tilberthwaite mines during this period. With gunpowder now in general use, the driving of tunnels and winning of ore was speeded up considerably.

By 1795 the Macclesfield Company workings had reached a depth in excess of three hundred feet below the surface and they decided, wrongly as it proved later, to abandon the mine as unproductive. The man who proved them wrong was John Taylor, the famous mining engineer, who had extensive experience in the mining fields of Devon, Cornwall and Derbyshire. He came to Coniston in 1824 and was to transform the mines into the largest and most profitable copper mines in the north. John Taylor signed a lease with the landowner, Lady le Fleming of Rydal Estates, giving him the rights to "use all lawful means for the finding, discovering, winning, working or getting mines of copper ore and minerals within the Lordship of Coniston belonging to Anne le Fleming". A royalty of "one twelfth part of all washed metals or minerals to be gotten out of the mine" was payable.

Taylor was soon driving new access tunnels to the Bonsor Vein in Red Dell. One of these still bears his name, the other was named Flemings Level after Lady Anne le Fleming. Level driving was also proceeding in the Paddy End Mine below the old German workings. In 1825 Taylor started his most ambitious and expensive project, the driving of a deep adit level from the lowest practical point. This area, behind the present day youth hostel, became the main ore dressing floors in the Copper Mines Valley. The adit level became known as the Deep, or Horse Level, and eventually extended beneath the Red Dell (Bonsor) and Paddy End workings. Within the various branches it was to become one and a half miles long and de-watered the vast area of workings. It also served as an excellent tramway for horse-drawn wagons from all parts of the mine.

Taylor also constructed a system of leats to provide water power for winding, pumping and dressing. Water was drawn from Levers Water and Low Water and Red Dell and directed through up to three miles of leats, the same water powering water wheels at Triddle, Paddy End and at Bonsor Works.

On the 1st October, 1834 John Taylor signed a new lease to include Richard Gaunt and John Barratt. Barratt, formerly an employee, had now become a partner in the venture. He was appointed as mine manager. About this time work was started on what is now known as the Old Engine Shaft, which eventually replaced the Bonsor East Shaft used by Charles Roe. As the workings got deeper on the Bonsor Vein, more efficient means of extraction and pumping were required. Work was also underway on the Triddle Shaft and in 1844 the sinking of the New Engine Shaft was begun, along with the construction of the stone incline, which is still used today by fell walkers. Meanwhile at Paddy End further extensive development work was being carried out. In 1840 Levers Water Mine was started and it is recorded that 97 children were employed in mineral dressing in 1842, the youngest being six years old. The year of 1842 is significant in that the Mines Act was passed by the British Parliament, forbidding women and children to work underground.

It is perhaps appropriate at this point to quote extracts from a contemporary account written by Dr Alexander Craig Gibson, who was the medical officer at the mines between 1844 and 1851. It was written in 1848 and provides a fascinating insight into the working methods and conditions at the time.

High up on the mountainside, you may notice a solitary waterwheel which, from having nothing near it visible from below, appears to be spinning away like a child's toy mill without aim or object. It is at the top of the main shaft, and is employed in hoisting those kibbles and water to the horse level.

And now having arrived at the works, before examining the details of the dressing process, suppose you take a subterranean ramble, and see how and where the ore is obtained, and to do that comfortably, it were well to borrow some regular habiliments to save your clothes – the gentlemen below stairs will excuse your appearing amongst them in full dress.

It will be wise to select the oldest and most extensive part of the mines for exploration, and it is that most to the east, so when you are properly equipped and have procured candles and a guide, proceed at once to the horse level mouth, light your candles, open the door and walk in.

When you have progressed thus with your crest lowered for some distance, you may straight your back and look up, for you are under the 'Cobblers hole' a tremendous chasm, from which a vein of copper, extending to above the water-wheel you saw on the hill-side, has been wrought, and when you are advanced about a quarter of a mile into the level, you are at the side of the shaft which reaches from the said water-wheel through all the workings down to the deepest level, and by which kibbles containing the ore are hoisted a few fathoms above your head, and there emptied into a large hopper, the mouth of which is six or seven feet above the level, and under it the wagons are run to be loaded. If you are determined to descend the shaft, it must be by a series of ladders, with wooden sides and iron steps, and you come to a platform,

or 'landing' at every few fathoms. Diverging occasionally from but generally following the line of the shaft, you pass several old 'bunnins' – I am not sure about orthography, but the derivation is, I fancy, from 'bound in' – which are short logs of wood jammed between the opposite walls of rock for the miners to stand upon when working in such situations. As you proceed on your perilous journey, you must not allow the thundering echoes of the distant blast, or the astounding rattle of the rapidly descending kibble and its chain, to deprive you of your presence of mind, else you are 'but a dead tourist'. But supposing that you carry your senses along with you, and are resolved to stop at nothing short of the deep workings, you continue, sometimes crawling down the ladder, and sometimes stepping cautiously across the landings, you pass several levels in your descent – viz, one twenty fathoms down, one thirty-five, one fifty, and at length you arrive at the seventy fathom, when you are somewhere about the level of the village, or about four hundred and twenty feet below the place where you commenced your underground knight errantry – or, again, about six hundred and forty feet below the top of the shaft. There is, 'at the lowest depth a lower still', some twenty fathoms below this, another working, called 'the ninety', but you are already deep enough for any useful purpose. Moving a short way onwards, you come in sight of two men working upon a 'bunnin', and looking, according to your notion, very much like the inhabitants of a still lower region, the darkness being made barely visible by a couple of twinkling candles plastered against the rock with clay. Their attitudes are somewhat picturesque, as they hold up and turn the jumper with the left hand, whilst they keep driving it into the flinty rock by an incessant rapping with a hammer held in the right. Having bored their holes to a sufficient depth, they proceed to clear them out with an iron instrument something like a yard long needle, with its point bent and flattened – first scraping out the borings or fragments of stone, with the point, and then drying the hole with a small wisp of straw, or dried grass, drawn through the eye and worked up and down in the hole until all the moisture is completely mopped up. They then fill a tin tube with gunpowder, and conveying it into the hole withdraw the tube and leave the hole filled to one third, or one half its depth with powder. Having corked down, by way of wadding, the wisp used in drying, and carefully cleaned away any stray grains of powder which may possibly adhere to the sides, they next thrust a long sharpened rod of copper, called a 'pricker' down one side into the powder, and pass an iron 'stemmer', or ramrod, grooved on one side to fit the pricker, to feel whether it worked easily, which it will not do, if the pricker is improperly inserted. They then beat in with the stemmer, a quantity of soft rotten stone called 'stemming', sufficient to fill up the hole, finishing off with a little clay, and commence with the withdrawal of the pricker, an operation of some nicety. Having got it out, they pass down the hole it leaves a long straw filled with powder, having a piece of match paper attached to its outer extremity and having secured their tools, and uttered two or three indescribable warning shouts, the precise sounds of which it is difficult to realise, but which consist of the monosyllable 'fire', they ignite the touch papers and immediately retire to a respectable distance, and you have better retire with them, to await the report, which, when it does occur, will be pretty likely to make you jump an inch or two out of your skin. Returning to their working, they note

carefully the effects of the blast, and breaking up larger fragments, and beating down any loose pieces that may hang about the sides, they select a suitable 'lofe' and recommence boring. About three blasts in this hard rock is considered a fair day's work, the men working eight hours a day in shifts – which does not mean that they array themselves in chemises to work in, but that they are relieved or shifted at the end of eight hours, by other workmen taking their places.

And now having visited the depth of the mines, and witnessed the most important, as well as the most common of the underground operations, and moreover, being almost 'sconfished' with the powder smoke, you are anxious to return to the blessed light of day, and 'heaven's untainted breath', and may clamber up the interminable ladders you descended by. What you have seen, of course, conveys no adequate idea of the extent of the mines, for these hills are almost honeycombed by levels and other workings, but you have seen enough to show you the nature of copper mining. It is rather extraordinary that the mines, even in their deepest parts, are infested by myriads of rats, and why they harbour there, or what they get to eat, would require a longer head than mine to discover.

It says much for the excellent arrangements on the part of the management, that, notwithstanding the dangerous nature of the work, and the number of hands employed, serious accidents are of very rare occurrence, and when they do occur, they are almost always the result of negligence, frequently involving disobedience of orders, on the part of the sufferer. However one of the most melancholy that has yet occurred, was purely accidental, and I may relate it as a

95

sad episode in mining life. A father and son – Irishmen – named Redmond, were employed at the foot of a shaft, 'filling kibbles'. The father's kibble had descended, and he had unhooked the chain, handing it to his son to attach to his kibble, which was full, and commenced refilling, when his attention was attracted by a cry, and, starting round, he saw his son carried with the kibble rapidly up the dark shaft. He called to him to hold on by the bucket, but that was considered hopeless by the workmen about, because the shaft is tortuous and the sides very rugged and uneven. A very short time showed that they were correct, for the unfortunate youth's body was heard tumbling down the shaft. The old man placed himself below, stretching out his arms to catch the body as it fell, and was with difficulty dragged from the position where he would have shared the fate of his son, whose mangled body fell close to his feet.

Another story of a different character connected with kibble filling, I may tell you by way of light relief to the above sad narrative. A man was employed in this department, who had seen better days, and whose thoughtlessness or ill luck had reduced him to labour thus for his daily bread, but whose humour and ready wit were by no means impaired by his fallen fortunes. One of the agents observing some small stones falling down the shaft said 'Take care – or you will have your brains knocked out'. He continued his work replying coolly, 'If I had ever had any brains, Captain, I should not have been here'.

And now, having safely returned to this everyday world, you may examine the processes through which the ore has to pass, before it is fit for the market, for, unlike most other mining, one half of the work is not done when it is brought above ground. Well, first, you perceive, it is thrown from the wagons into a heap, where water runs over it, and by cleaning the lumps, shows more plainly what each piece is made of. Then from the heap it is raked by men to a platform, or long low bench, along which a number of little boys are actively engaged in picking or separating the richer pieces from the poorer, and it is highly amusing to watch the expertness and celerity with which the imps make the selection and toss each lump into its proper receptacle. The richest portion is carried at once to the crushing mill, the poorer is thrown into another shed below, to be broken up and further picked, and the mere stones are wheeled off to the rubbish heap. The ore being broken small is thrown into a crushing mill, and passed once or twice through it, being returned to the mill by an endless chain of iron buckets, which dip into the heap of crushed ore below, and carry it up, empty themselves into the mill. When ground to the size of coarse sand, the ore is carried to the 'jigging troughs', which are large square boxes, filled with water, and having each a smaller box, with a grated bottom, suspended in it to a beam above, and filled with ore, a 'jiggin' motion being imparted to the grated boxes by water power. This jigging under the water causes the grains of pure ore, which are heavy, to sink and pass through the grating of the inner box, and the particles of spar and rock, which are lighter, to rise to the top, where they are scouped off and wheeled away to undergo another pounding and washing. The pounding is effected by means of two long rows of stamps or heavy iron shod pestles, kept incessantly rising and falling in beds fronted with perforated iron plates, and fed with material, and a flow of water to wash it, when fine enough, through the holed *plate. It is, after that, collected to go through the process of 'buddling', which consists of laying it on slanted shelves, at the head of long wooden troughs, also slanting longitudinally, and a limited stream of water, being allowed to run through it and wash it slowly off the shelves and down the inclined troughs, the heavier and valuable portion remains at the head, whilst the lighter and worthless portion is washed down to the lower end. All the waste water used in any of the dressing processes is made to flow through a series of large tanks or reservoirs, in which it deposits all the fine particles of ore that may be floating away, and from these tanks some thousands of pounds worth of ore is collected annually in the form of slime, and looking like bronze, which with all the other ore, is shipped to Swansea to be smelted.*

Elsewhere in Lakeland copper mines were on the decline once again. Goldscope was still working but producing only lead. A small tonnage of copper was recorded from the Roughton Gill mines at this time (1840s), but most of the ore extracted here was also lead. The Copperplate Mine in Borrowdale was re-opened but little was done. Birkside Gill Mine above the waterfall north of Dunmail Raise was in production, as were two small copper mines near the northern end of Hawes Water.

Much prospecting was going on in the Duddon Valley at the following mines – Seathwaite Tarn, Cockley Beck, Logan Beck, Hesk Fell and Ulpha Copper Mine. The last two named were probably the only ones to show profit.

At Coniston the mine was reaching its peak period. In 1849 the workings were down to 90 fathoms (540 feet) below Deep Level. The following year John Barratt

began driving another deep level, this one in Tilberthwaite, which was to de-water the extensive old workings in the high valley to the east of Wetherlam. This level, also named Barratt's Level, was 3000 feet long and took ten years to complete.

1856 was the year of the highest production figures for Coniston mines. Output was 3659 tons of ore valued at £27,861. In 1858 an anonymous hand-written essay, entitled 'Coniston Mine' gives us yet another detailed glimpse of the mine some ten years after Dr Gibson's account. The following is an extract and the original spelling has been adhered to.

Next came the Barratts which worked the mines on a large scale. They drove the deep adit level til they cut the load and then sunk the old shaft which is 1020 ft from the Adit, 300 ft more from the grass roots. The work was lifted by water power the big water wheel which was 44 ft 7 in high 9ft across the breast weight 21 tons 11 cwt and 65 Horse power. the water was pumped up in 4 lifts the Bottom lift was a draw lift And the other 3 were plungers 300 ft apart. Every 40 yards down there was a drift set of which went from one shaft and the other that was 4 Stoops high that ment 10 Stoops at the rate of 4 men to Every working.

Inside men was close on 700 the work was drawn out from under ground by Horse power and then it was dressed by men and boys and women and girls which there was about 50 women and about 300 men and boys the copper raised was about 5 or 6 hundred tons a month.

The work was drawn out at the rate of 8 trips a shift with 3 big Iron waggons which held 2 tons Each then it was dumpted down a Screen which sized it into 3 sections then it was sorted into 4 lots the first was the solid ore which was put out by itself the next was what was called Douse it was the second best the third was class quartze and copper mixed which had to go through the crushing mill to be ground to a find sand then it taken to the water sives there were 6 sets of them with 2 sives to Every Set. Each set of tubs was Emptied twice a week and Each set of tubs held 5 tons that ment 60 tons a week of jigged ore then it was put into a pile and the solid pile was ground and thrown over it so that they got an avarage sample. After that it was All turned over a weighed and then carted to Coniston Hall and taken to Nibthwaite by boat and then carted to Ulverston and put on rail and sent to Sent Elens.

It is interesting to learn of the rapidly deepening Old Engine Shaft, now down to 1020 feet below Deep Level, which is 100 feet below sea level. At approximately every 20 fathoms, (120 feet), levels were driven off to extract the ore from the Bonsor Vein.

The figures quoted for those employed in the mines seem rather high. Over the previous twenty years many cottages had been built in rows overlooking Coniston village to house the mining families, but they would hardly accommodate an extra 1000 people as suggested in the essay.

The mines were so productive that it was decided in 1858 to construct a branch line from the Furness Railway at Foxfield thus doing away with the slow, laborious carting and boating of the ore via Coniston Water to Ulverston Canal. This means of transport had been in use since the destruction of the Keswick smelters in the mid-seventeenth century. The railway line opened on 18th June 1859. During the 1860s the output of copper ore began an irreversible decline. In 1860 it was less than 3000 tons of dressed copper per annum and four years later had dipped below 2000 tons. The workings on the great Bonsor Vein were so deep that the cost of maintaining services, hoisting, timberwork and pumping, etc. was mounting. Up to sixteen waterwheels were said to be operating around 1870. To add to the problems, an increasing amount of magnetite was mixed with the ore below the 170 fathom level, which was very difficult to separate during dressing operations at that time.

Elsewhere in the Lake District, copper mining had almost ceased. Carrock End Mine had produced copper in 1863 and Red Gill Mine had raised only 45 tons of dressed copper ore between 1861 and 1871. The famous Roughton Gill Mine struggled on suffering heavy losses due to extensive but fruitless development work and finally closed in 1878.

The miners of old had missed very little in their search for minerals in the Lakeland hills and dales over the centuries, but there is a location known to the author which seems to have gone unnoticed. A fairly strong vein of copper carbonate (malachite) outcrops on the south wall of Easy Gully on Dow Crags, two kilometres south west of Paddy End mines.

The fate of copper mining in Lakeland was sealed in the 1880s when cheap imported ore was brought from foreign lands. This coincided with the introduction of compressed air drills at Coniston in 1883, where the workings had now reached a depth of 205 fathoms (1230 feet) below Deep Level Adit. Dynamite had also been in use since 1877, but these valuable advances in technology were of no avail. The Old Engine Shaft wheel was stopped for the last time in 1897 after the robbing of ore pillars below Deep Level had been carried out, leaving the mine in a dangerous state. In the same year the New Engine Shaft wheel and associated machinery was dismantled. Extraction of any ore left in the higher and older workings, both at Paddy End and Red Dell carried on until the turn of the century. Again it was a case of removing supporting pillars and floors where the veins had been left for reasons of safety.

In 1908 a French company set up an electrolytic plant to process the extensive spoil heaps. This lasted until the outbreak of the First World War in 1914. The remaining water wheels were removed for scrap in the 1930s, the last in 1939 from the Bonsor Upper Mill. Apart from some prospecting work carried out in the early 1950s nothing more has been done. The mines were left to decay – a permanent reminder of the prosperous past, of the employment they provided and the influence they had on the development of various Lakeland communities and Coniston village in particular.

The visitor to Lakeland today may still see much evidence of past copper mining activity in the area, mainly in the form of spoil heaps, tunnels, shafts and ruined mine buildings. Coniston mines are now scheduled by English Heritage as an historical monument. This legislation was implemented after a developer purchased the Upper Bonsor Mill dressing floors and associated ruined mine buildings and then commenced construction work and excavations without planning consent.

There is plenty to see relating to the 19th century period of operation, including the mine office, now the Youth Hostel, and the mine foreman's house and stables, now a mountaineering club headquarters. Behind these are the settling ponds and many ruined buildings which included a saw mill, the

mine laboratory, a carpenter's shop and waterwheel pits, etc. Other waterwheel pits at Bonsor East and the Old and New Engine Shafts are worth visiting. The stone arched entrance portals to Gaunts Level and Deep Level adit are still intact.

Since 1980 Cumbria Amenity Trust Mining History Society has been very active in exploring, surveying and conserving the underground workings. Prior to this, small independent groups had been active but it became evident that a larger, well-equipped and co-ordinated organisation was required. Cumbria Amenity Trust has made many interesting discoveries deep within long forgotten tunnels and workings. Numerous artefacts were found, exactly as the miners left them. These included ore wagons, railways and points, windlasses, a shaft kibble, winding wheels and amongst the smaller items were shovels, hammers, drills, prickers, tin water bottles, ore sacks, clogs, clay pipes, candles, etc.

In the Top Level workings at Paddy End there are still hundreds of feet of skilfully made wooden ventilation trunkings. Some of the pumping rods remain in position in the Old Engine Shaft. The most intriguing discovery was perhaps that of a joiner-made oak barrier or dam sealing a tunnel beneath Levers Water, which can only be reached with great difficulty. A legend had been passed down over several generations in Coniston village, which spoke of two oak plugs used to seal Levers Water from the mine when the tarn was dammed and the water level raised. The story was not really believed, but on the 25th January, 1987 it was proved to be correct when one oak barrier was discovered under the tarn.

It is recorded in Sir Daniel Fleming's account books for the Coniston forge that "William and Thomas Dixon did four days work in November 1682 mending the dam at Levers Water", but it is unlikely that the oak barrier is that old.

In a letter dated 11th June 1844 written by John Taylor to his partner Richard Gaunt, it is stated that "due to drought conditions they are raising the dam at Leverswater". This is possibly when the oak barriers were installed. After over 150 years they continue to hold back the waters of the reservoir.

Without doubt the most spectacular sights in these mines would never have been seen by the miners of old. For well over a hundred years, formations have been growing on the walls and floors of the workings in the form of blue and green copper carbonate 'flowstone' deposits. The finest of these very colourful 'static cascades' is to be found in the remote inner reaches of Taylors Level and in Levers Water Mine.

In recent years Cumbria Amenity Trust has worked in conjunction with English Heritage and the Lake District National Park Authority towards the conservation of these historic mines. In addition assistance was given to the Historical Monuments Commission during their detailed survey of the surface remains. The Society is currently engaged in compiling a detailed survey of the complex underground workings at the request of the British Geological Survey. All this is for the benefit of future historians and researchers of industrial archaeology.

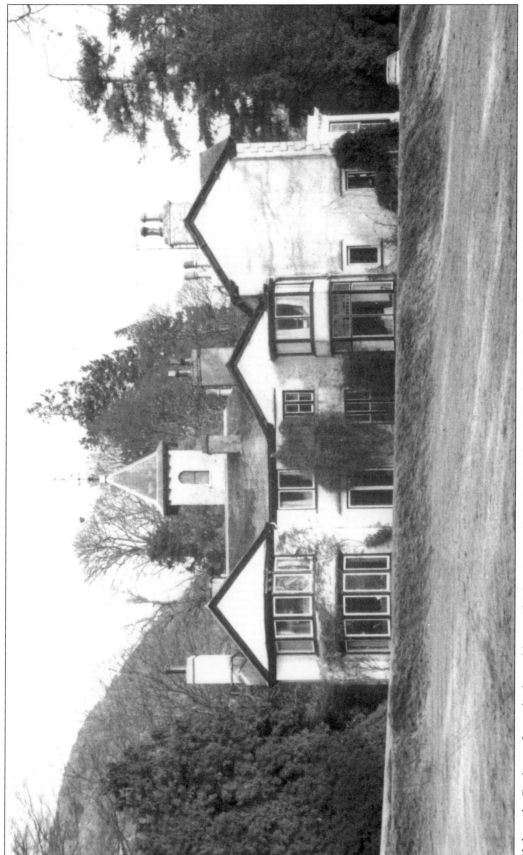

Holywath, Coniston, formerly the residence of John Barratt, the principal shareholder in the Coniston Copper Mines. Barratt purchased the house in 1842 for £265, when it was no more than a cottage. He enlarged the building over a period of time. It is still the home of one of John Barratt's descendants, Major J W Barratt Hext.

Photo: *Peter Fleming*

The Old Engine Shaft Waterwheel, as it appeared in 1908. The original 30ft diameter wheel was installed in 1834, the larger one illustrated here was 45ft in diameter and was fitted by John Barratt in 1850.

Photo provided by: *Peter Fleming*

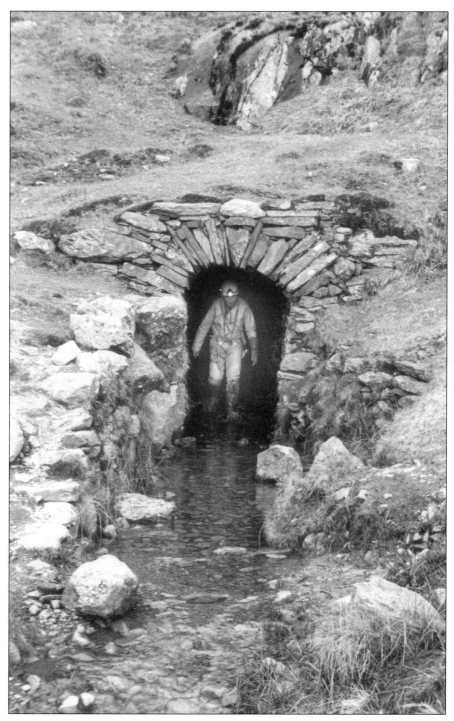

The Bonsor Deep Level, or Horse Level, was driven in 1825 under the direction of the famous mining engineer, John Taylor, to intercept the Bonsor Vein, a quarter of a mile inside the southern flank of Wetherlam. Water from the deep Bonsor workings was pumped by waterwheel and reciprocating rods to discharge into the new level and flow out into Red Dell Beck. With the sinking of the Old Engine Shaft, and later the New Engine Shaft, Deep Level became the major water course of the Red Dell workings. In later years the underground ramifications of Red Dell and Paddy End were connected by an extension of the Deep Level, driven through the soft rock of the Great Crosscourse. In its entirety, Deep Level was somewhere in the region of one-and-a-half miles in length, its branches penetrating most of the major veins of the area.

Photo: *Peter Fleming*

The Old Engine Shaft waterwheel - 45 feet in diameter, 100 hp, installed in 1850 was last used in 1897. It replaced an earlier 30ft diameter wheel known as the Threadle Wheel which was installed in 1834 by John Taylor.

A - Wooden launder from water race
B - Winding machinery house
C - Winding rope or chain
D - Signal wire to shaft
E - Driving rod via rocking post to flat rods
F - Flat rods to balance bob
G - Sheaved winding wheel
H - Wooden shaft partition
J - Pumping rods
K - Weight box

Arrangement of the balance bob at the top of the Old Engine Shaft. This shaft, 1320 feet deep, was used for haulage and pumping, and contained a laddered manway below Deep Level.

Drawings: *Peter Fleming*

A kibble, used for hauling ore and waste from the depths of the workings. This particular example, made from two plates of iron rivetted together, was rescued from Taylor's Level. For an idea of the scale, the clay pipe is 102 mm long. This kibble is small compared with the kibbles used in the larger shafts, some of which were capable of holding over a ton of ore.

What appears at first sight to be just a lump of Borrowdale volcanic is in fact an early stone mortar for hand-crushing copper ore. These mortar stones, sometimes called ore-dressing stones or anvils, were in use over a very long period of time. Similar stones were used in the Bronze Age workings on Great Ormes Head, Anglesey, and on the 19th century lead dressing floors at Eagle Crag Mine, Patterdale. Dating implements such as these is virtually impossible, though expert opinion maintains that this particular example pre-dates the Elizabethan period. For scale – the clay pipe (discovered in a near-by slate quarry) is 102 mm long.

Photo: *Peter Fleming*

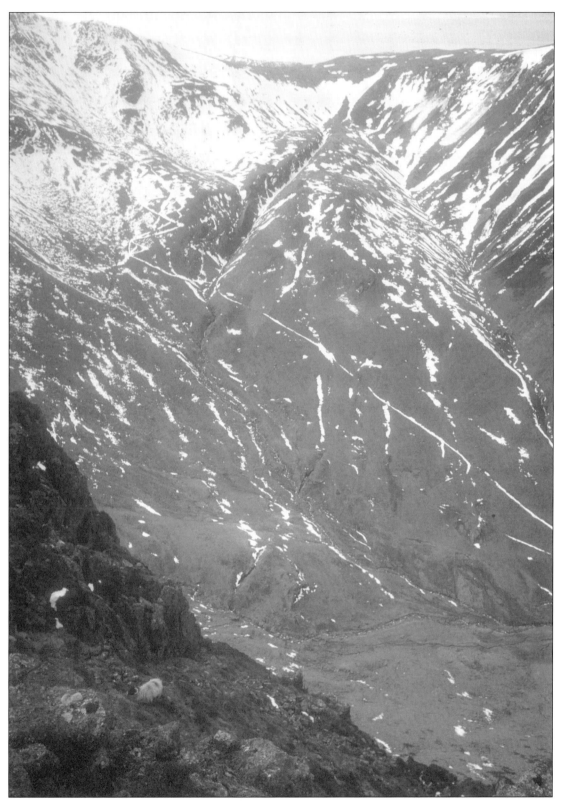

At the head of Newlands Valley a zig-zag miners' track leads up to Dale Head copper mine situated about 1800ft (550m) above sea level. Close by the mine on the exposed hillside can be found the remains of a small dressing floor and smithy.

Photo: *David Bridge*

In about the year 1600 the Company of Mines Royal erected a waterwheel inside Goldscope Copper Mine to pump out and raise ore from the workings below adit level. The wheel was fed from a reservoir in Scope Beck at the site shown here and the leat ran beneath the western flank of Hindscarth for ¾ mile (over 1 km). The dam was rebuilt in Victorian times to supply water to a 40ft diameter wheel designed to de-water the newly discovered rich Goldscope Lead Vein.

Photo: *David Bridge*

The 540ft long Horse Crag Deep Adit started by John Barratt in about 1850 and completed in 1869 was driven to intersect the Tilberthwaite copper veins at depth and Penny Rigg Mill was constructed adjacent to the adit mouth and operated by the Coniston and Tilberthwaite Mining Company. The mill was powered by two waterwheels of 12ft and 32ft diameter but the mine's disappointing output never fully justified its construction.

Photo: *David Bridge*

Top Level, within the Coniston Coppermines was nearly half a mile long and had no natural ventilation. This wooden trunking was installed to provide air at the working face and to disperse the fumes and dust after blasting. Air would be forced along the trunking either by a manually driven fan (usually operated by one of the mine boys) or by a water-blast system.

Photo: *Ian Matheson*

Standing like a watch tower in the throat of Red Dell, the launder support for the Old Engine Shaft waterwheel is all that remains to mark the site of Coniston's largest wheel. The shaft was sunk by John Taylor around 1834 to exploit the chalcopyrite of the Bonsor Vein. For many years the great stopes of the Bonsor had been pumped dry by the wheel of the Bonsor East Shaft, situated a few yards to the left of the picture. But the Bonsor East shaft was sunk on the vein and its route, as the mine deepened, became tortuous and the pump-rods inefficient. The Old Engine Shaft was sunk to the north of the vein and descended vertically through the hard Borrowdale volcanics to intercept the mineralised ground at a depth of several hundred feet. The shaft top was situated at the end of a short tunnel a few yards to the north of the wheel pit. The reciprocating rods ran on rollers to an angle-bob, from which descended the heavy pitch-pine pump-rods, delivering motion to the pumps over a thousand feet below. The pump-rods are still in position in the upper reaches of the shaft – and the sheave winding wheel (the waterwheel also provided the motion for raising the ore) still sits in a cradle of timber above the shaft top.

Photo: *Peter Fleming*

This notice was installed within the past 10 years to warn of the dangers beyond. The location is the point at which Deep Level Adit intersects the Bonsor East Shaft in the Coniston Mine. The shaft below this point is flooded to over 1000ft. whilst the workings above are full of loose and unstable mine debris. Perhaps not a place to linger!

Photo: *Ian Matheson*

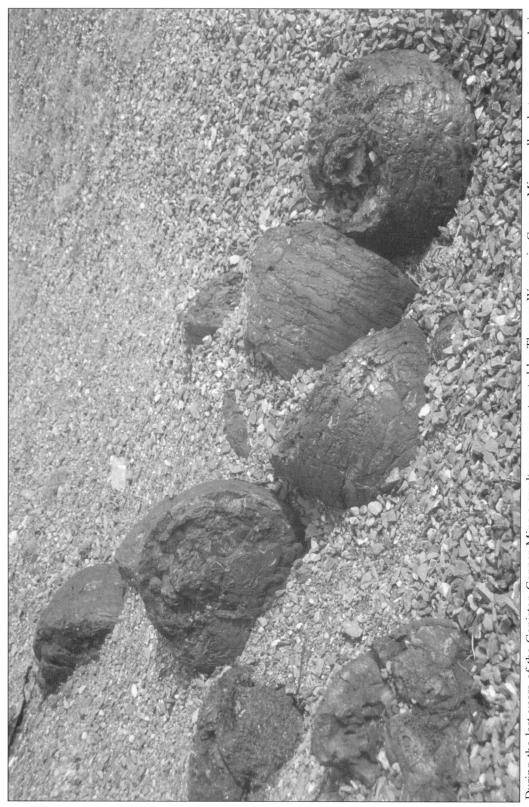

During the last years of the Coniston Copper Mine a smelter was constructed by Thomas Warsop in Copper Mines valley, but a severe gale in December 1894 wrecked the buildings and plant before commissioning was complete and the smelter was never rebuilt. These 2ft diameter slag bowls discarded beside the track to the copper mines remain as a reminder of the venture.

Photo: *David Bridge*

At some copper mining sites in the Lake District, notably the Paddy End workings by Levers Water, mortar stones used for crushing the ore by hand have been discovered. This one was recently identified at the old dressing floor of Dale Head Mine at the head of Newlands Valley near Keswick.

Photo: *David Bridge*

Within Honister Crag the Honister Internal Incline serves several slate levels. At each horizon slate could be loaded onto the incline carrier. To allow waste slate rock to be taken beyond the incline and out onto the face of the Crag a hinged wooded bridge was lowered over the track. The Honister Crag Incline is possibly the last counterbalanced incline in (more or less) working order in England.

Photo: *Ian Matheson*

LAKELAND'S MINING HERITAGE – BARYTES

by Alen McFadzean and Ian Tyler

Unlike copper, lead, iron and coal, the common minerals of the county, barytes has been mined as a commercial product only since recent times. Prior to the mid 18th century it was of little value to the mining companies and was, along with calcite, quartz, and other gangue minerals, thrown over the tips as a waste material. Nowadays barytes is in great demand for a variety of purposes and the Lake District mines have, in recent decades, produced many thousands of tons. Lakeland's barytes industry, though, terminated in 1990 when Force Crag – the last working mine – was forced to close after a serious collapse in Zero Level brought production to a halt. Mining still continues on a small scale in the Cumbrian Pennines, where the mineral is worked from an opencast at Silverband Mine.

Barytes (barium sulphate, $BaSO_4$), or barite as it is sometimes called, varies in colour from a bluish-yellow to brown and red. It has a glassy lustre, is usually opaque, and commonly comprises tabular, equidimensional crystals, in masses or featherlike formations. It often forms the gangue material of sulphide ore veins which is how it occurs locally – though in sedimentary rocks it manifests as nodules and free-growing crystals.

Some of the finest barytes specimens ever discovered have come from the mining fields of Cumbria. Single crystals, some of them eight inches in length, have been won from the local mines. But the mineral occurs in a variety of forms throughout the world. Near Norman, Oklahoma, barytes is found in the form of desert roses and in perfect imitation of the flower; while near Stirling, Colorado, it occurs as blue crystals in the local sediments. In Rumania, in the mines of the Felsobanya region, barytes occurs as flat, yellowish crystals intermingled with stibnite. It has been mined extensively in Europe, where it is found in association with other minerals, notably sphalerite.

Perfect crystals of barytes have been discovered in association with sphalerite in the lower levels of Force Crag Mine, Coledale, near Keswick. Here the mineral forms the vein material, but in the course of mining many large natural cavities, or vugs, have been discovered, the walls of which have been adorned with splendid specimens. In the mines of Alston, transparent crystals have been found, though more commonly barytes occurs locally as a pale, featureless mineral resembling gypsum, felspar and calcite, from which it can be determined by hardness and weight. Indeed, it was in regard to the latter characteristic (with a specific gravity of 4.48) that the miners christened it 'heavy spar'.

Its uses in today's chemical industry are manifold. It is added to paint products as a lead substitute and forms a pigment in the preparation of lithopone. Barytes mud is used extensively in the oil exploration industry where it adds weight to the special drilling lubricants in deep boreholes. It is mixed with concrete in the construction of nuclear installations, and provides the substance of a barium meal for internal x-rays. It has been, and still is, used as a filler in the cloth and paper industries; and if local tradition is to be relied on, has been mixed with flour by the miserly millers of Braithwaite.

Mines in which barytes has been present as a vein ore, and worked as a commercial mineral, include Blencathra Mine, Ruthwaite Mine, Potts Gill Mine, Sandbeds Mine, Force Crag Mine and the mines of the Cross Fell area. Barytes has also been present as gangue mineral in Greenside and Hartsop Hall mines, in Patterdale and at Wythburn Mine, Thirlmere.

Force Crag has been one of the main producers, though when the mine was first investigated in 1755 it was galena – the mineral ore of lead – not barytes that proved to be the attraction. It was to be some time, over a hundred years in fact, before the gleaming white spar was to command its own market – as Postlethwaite, writing in 1889 in his *Mines and Mining in the English Lake District*, illustrates.

The deposits of sulphate barytes which occur in the Force Crag vein are amongst the most remarkable mineral deposits that have been found in the Skiddaw slates; they commonly measure from three to five feet in thickness, and one was found in 1872 which measured ten feet in thickness. Some of the barytes is very pure and white; but a great deal is coloured by the psilomelane with which it is associated, and with iron.

The psilomelane also occurs in considerable quantities, but very little of it can be obtained in a pure state.

The mine was opened up, or probably reopened, by Mr Walton of Alston, and Messrs Dowthwaite & Cowper, of Keswick, and others, about eighty years ago; there is no definite information on this point, but the author can remember that in

the year 1846 [sic – 1848] some of the proprietors had become tired of their enterprise and the mine was stopped three months in order that the company might be wound up, and a fresh lease taken out in the names of those who were prepared to carry on the work, which they did for about thirty years, and succeeded in raising a large quantity of ore.

Messrs Walton & Co paid very little attention to the barytes, as it was scarcely saleable during the greater part of their tenure; but in later years it has been more extensively used in the manufacture of plate glass, and for the more questionable purpose of adulterating white lead, consequently the mineral has been in greater demand.

After a short interval of inactivity the mine was taken up again by a company of local gentlemen, for the purpose of raising barytes. They commenced operations in the low level, but afterwards discovered that the mineral was much more plentiful higher up the mountain; therefore, the old mine was abandoned, and two more levels were driven still higher up the mountain, and large deposits of barytes discovered.

And so, like the majority of Lakeland mines, Force Crag's history developed as a series of intensive working periods and interludes of abandonment. The upper reaches of the mine, High Force, situated above the 2,000 ft contour on the steep slopes of Grisedale Pike, were worked exclusively for barytes, the galena and sphalerite being extracted from the lower levels of the mine. Today, several decades after the upper mine was abandoned, it is still possible to examine the worked out stopes and study the techniques employed by the barytes miners of yesteryear.

The main vein at Force Crag is vertical by nature though dips slightly to the north. It has been worked by a series of levels driven from the fellside, intersecting the mineral over a series of heights. As with most Lakeland mineral mines, once the levels had been driven they were then linked internally by a series of shafts and ladderways, to aid the extraction of the mineral and facilitate the movement of men and equipment from one level to another.

One of the interesting features of the Lakeland barytes mines, which puts them apart from the other mineral workings, is the wide adoption of the pillar system. The veins were stoped away leaving huge blocks of mineral in situ to enhance the stability of the mine. In some areas of Force Crag, and particularly in High Force, the pillars have been robbed, leaving parts of the mine in a dangerous condition. Many pillars still remain, spanning the dark stopes with broad sections of gleaming white and yellow barytes, allowing an insight into the richness and impressive width of the barytes veins.

Mineral was removed from the veins with high explosives. Once dislodged it was allowed to lie in the floor of the stope prior to being drawn off from the tramming level below through wooden hoppers. Again, most mineral mines used hoppers in this manner, though the barytes industry appears to have been particularly suited to this mode of extraction. Extensive batteries of wooden hoppers were built in the tramming levels of Potts Gill and Sandbeds, the rich barytes mines of the Caldbeck fells. And in High

Force the batteries of the 1100 ft Level, and the miniature hoppers in the narrow 650 ft Level, emphasise the fact that not only was mining an industry for skilled and knowledgeable men of the rock, it also encouraged the craft of woodworking and allowed no end of scope for creative genius.

In the upper levels of High Force stand a pair of wooden towers, wedged firmly between the walls of the stope but resembling those transportable siege towers

of medieval Europe. They were built by craftsmen during the early years of the 20th century to act as manways between tramming levels. At one time, and particularly during periods of activity, they would have been access routes when the walls of the original internal shafts had been robbed away and the stopes were lying deep in mineral waiting to be drawn off from below. Now the stopes are empty, robbed of their mineral. The hoppers have been drawn and the towers stand alone – monuments to the men who made them.

Similar wooden structures, known as mills, were erected in the Caldbeck barytes mines. In certain instances, where the ore was extracted by the 'cut and fill' method, these wooden ore-passes were built above the hoppers as the stopes gradually filled with waste material. One obvious advantage of this method of working was that dead rock could be stacked underground. Blasted veinstone was sorted where it fell, the ore being thrown down the mill, the waste left in the floor of the stope. As the roof of the stope ascended and the waste deepened, the mills were extended. This technique was employed at several locations in the county, notably the Threlkeld lead mines, and in the mines of the Alston area. In most instances the mills were constructed of masonry for added strength and many superb examples still exist in the north Pennine ore-fields. Locally, there are masonry-lined mills in the far reaches of Force Crag's No 1 Level and in the vein workings of Rachel Wood lead mine at Thornthwaite.

Caldbeck was the other main barytes mining area of the Lake District fells. Situated in a two-mile area of decomposed Borrowdale volcanic rock on the north side of High Pike, the barytes lodes course across the fell in an east-west direction, cutting the many copper and lead veins for which the Caldbeck fells are famous. Mining started in earnest in the 19th century, though undoubtedly the Elizabethan miners were aware of the existence of the beautiful heavy spar.

The main barytes producers were situated within the complex of workings between Fell Side and Calebrack. Old Potts Gill, and the ground around Sandbeds, Potts Gill and Deerhills, was opened as early as 1844, but the venture was not a success. A second attempt in the 1880s by the Cleator Moor Iron Company also failed to make any headway. Ruthwaite Mine, at Ireby, was first worked in 1869 and produced ore intermittently, under various companies, into the 20th century. But it was not until hard times swept the country during the lean years of the Great War that the barytes situation, generally, started to improve.

The Potts Gill mines worked on and off till the 1940s, when prospects were good for the Caldbeck fells and barytes mining took off in a big way. Driggith Mine, which had produced copper and lead, had been reopened for barytes in 1926 but came under new ownership no less than three times during the 1940s. East Potts Gill Mine commenced in 1942 for barytes and soon this essential war mineral for munitions was being produced from the Back Vein where barytes formed a rib a full six feet in width. The outcrop of Sandbeds East was discovered in 1927 but exploration and production did not proceed till 1946. Sandbeds West Mine, which was a continuation of the lodes worked in Sandbeds East, was not discovered till 1956.

The veins varied in width from a few inches to twenty feet, though not all the filling was barytes. The main gangue mineral was quartz, with barytes averaging a thickness of just under two feet. Some 150,000 tons of dressed barytes were produced from the mines of Caldbeck. Operations ceased in 1966 with the closure of the Sandbeds mines.

East Cumbria

There have also been trials and small barytes mines in the outlying areas of the Lake District, such as at Gilcrux and Ireby, near Cockermouth. Barytes mining, though, developed into a sizeable industry in the eastern borders of the county. The western slopes of the Pennine hills have numerous steep-sided valleys, created during the ice ages by glacial action which revealed the mineral veins.

The mined area commences in the north at Hartside and follows the escarpment down through the Hilton and Appleby area to Brough. No less than fourteen major veins have been worked for lead, barytes, witherite and fluorspar. Many of the mines are to be found at the inhospitable region where Cross Fell and Dun Fell dominate the area. Here wind speed averages 50 to 60 mph.

A feature of the local barytes formation is that it forms in tabular translucent crystals. One of the largest ever discovered, mined at Dufton, weighed nearly a hundredweight and is now on display at the Geological Museum.

Mining started in this area during the 14th century. The veins were hushed to expose them at depth or worked by bell pits, with water drained off by adits. The London Lead Company worked the whole of this area from 1820 to 1880, exclusively for lead. Then interest in barytes increased and the area once again became active.

Hartside Mine is situated on the northern side of the Hartside Pass. The vein was first worked commercially for barytes by the Hedworth Barium Company. After the initial investigation the mine was taken over by the La Porte Company who invested quite heavily, developing the Harrison Level and laying an inclined tramway from the adit to the road. The barytes was then taken to the company mill at Silverband, some ten miles to the south. La Porte worked the mine from 1940 to 1946, during which time they produced 15,000 tons of dressed barytes.

Just below the summit of Dun Fell is to be found Silverband Mine, the last working mine in the western Pennines, and now encompassed by a nature reserve. Originally worked for galena by the London Lead Company, the first contemporary company was again La Porte, who worked the mine extensively for barytes, and between 1939 and 1963 produced a staggering 215,000 tons of dressed ore.

The mine, situated at an altitude of over 2,000 feet, presented the company with a transportation problem. This was solved by the erection of an aerial ropeway, three-and-a-half miles down to the plant, the remains of which are still visible. Much of the equipment was dismantled on La Porte's directions and the mine became derelict.

In 1970 the lease was acquired by H Taylor, who worked the mine with great vigour and produced 75,000 tons of barytes. In 1983 the mine came under the auspices of Cragg & Cutriss Ltd, who are now working high above the mill and opencasting the vein. The ore is milled on site then transported down the steep winding road in huge lorries to the valley below. The mine was taken over by Waitings Minerals in 1994 and is now being operated much the same way.

Just a few miles to the south of Silverband is the picturesque village of Dufton, whose rows of neat red sandstone cottages and manorial hall bear witness to more prosperous times. Three miles up the winding track Dufton Mine is to be found between the 2,000 and 2,300 ft contours. Like most of the mines in this area, Dufton Mine was originally worked by the London Lead Company until they shut it down in 1873.

One of the main adits was Atkinson's Level, which produced both lead and barytes. Between 1882 and 1899 the mine was worked exclusively for barytes, some 9,500 tons being produced. A little work was done during the 1914-18 war but in more recent times a company took the lease and worked the mine dumps, the mill processing some 200 tons per week until 1986. The lease was then taken over by Nor-West Holst Ltd in 1987: they worked the veins high on the fell by the opencast method. But the project was shelved more or less overnight and the workings landscaped. The site suffered badly and the original London Lead Company buildings, along with most of the modern plant, were buried.

Still further south, towards Appleby, lie the ancient mines of Hilton and Murton. Prior to the London Lead Company workings, 1824-1876, records indicate mining activity as early as the 14th century.

Barytes was mined when the Scordale Mining Company took the lease in 1896. In the first year of operation 70 tons of witherite were produced. At the end of their tenure, in 1906, the lease was taken by the Brough Baryte Company Ltd, who worked till 1912. The total barytes production between 1896 and 1912 was 7,194 tons.

The Scordale company took the lease again and worked till 1919 when the mine fell idle. The mine was taken over – for the last time – by Messrs W Wharton in 1930, who worked till 1939. Surprisingly, La Porte, who were working various other mines in the area, took out the lease but never actually mined any ore.

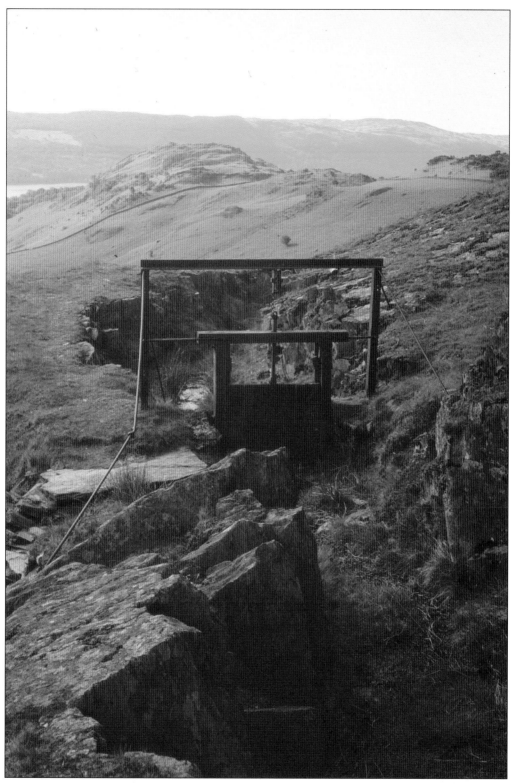

Water provided a readily available source of power for ore dressing at Coniston. Tongue Brow water race, some 600 yards long, was built to supply the Paddy End Mill with water from Red Dell. In the late 19th century, after pneumatic rock drills had been introduced, sluices diverted the water to a pelton wheel at the Bonsor Mill below for driving an air compressor.

Photo: *David Bridge*

Ventilation in mines was very important and the natural air currents rising up through the mine were controlled and directed by air tight doors, which were often manned by boys. This one in the Coniston Mine is in an inaccessible part of Deep Level.

Photo: *Ian Matheson*

This wrought iron shaft kibble, complete with its wooden base, was found, exactly as shown in the photograph, high up in the stopes above Deep Level in the Coniston Mine close to the New Engine Shaft. It had probably stood in this exact position for 120 years. The kibble was rescued and restored and is now on display in the Ruskin Museum, Coniston, along with other artefacts from the Mine.

This remarkably beautiful grotto was discovered in 1984 in Levers Water Mine, Coniston. All imaginable colours from white through green, blue and black are present. They are due to the many different minerals that have leached out of the surrounding rocks over the years.

Photos: *Peter Fleming*

In the second photograph work is in progress to stabilise the wheel and re-mount it so that it is in an upright position. All those working on the project were fully protected by ropes attached to firm belays.

Photo: *Mike Mitchell*

At the head of the Old Engine Shaft in the Coniston Copper Mines the winding wheel is still in place although in a precarious position. Clearly this important relic required stabilising to prevent it falling 1300ft down the shaft.

Photo: *Peter Fleming*

These two photographs show the final stages of repair of the Old Engine Shaft winding wheel supports.

Photos: *Mike Mitchell*

This photograph was taken high in the stopes of Paddy End Mine, seventy feet above the sole of Middle Level. Timbers, or stemples as they were called, were positioned at regular intervals to add support and prevent the stope walls from crashing in. They also provided convenient perches from which the miners could operate.

Photo: *Peter Fleming*

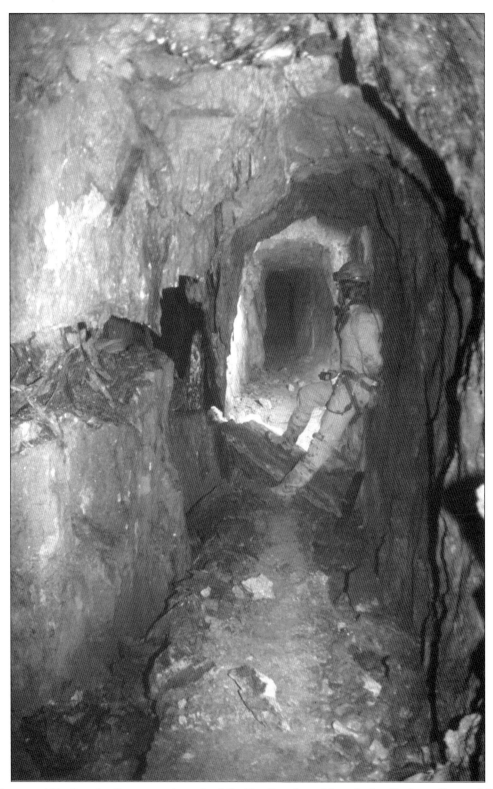

The aptly named Earthquake Passage, a branch of the Top Level workings in the Coniston Copper Mines, is a fine example of the effects of fracturing, caused by stress in the hard volcanic rock. The tunnel runs through a narrow band of rock separating the stopes of two parallel veins. The tunnel wall is slowly subsiding into the roof of the nearest stope.

Photo: *Peter Fleming*

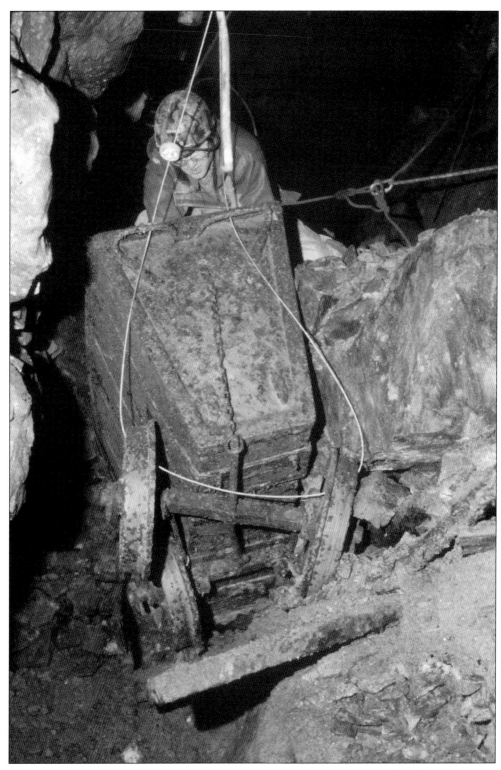

The ore tub shown here is one of three discovered in the Coniston Copper Mines and is thought to date from the 1880s. The design is interesting because the wheels are not equidistant from the ends. The front axle has been placed close to the centre of gravity to allow ease of tipping. The rear axle is not fixed to the chassis – it floats free to render the tub manoeuvrable in tight corners. The photographs show the ore tub being salvaged and, on the right, the tub after restoration installed on a purpose built section of rail.

Photos: *Mike Mitchell* and *Peter Fleming*

Although Goldscope Mine is the most important site of early copper working in the Newlands Valley near Keswick, several other hand-chiselled open works are in the area and are thought to date from the 16th century. This short 'open cut' below Little Mine Crag is a good example and shows clear evidence of the use of 'plug and feather'.

Photo: *David Bridge*

Another open cut in the Newlands Valley is known as St Thomas's Work. The early miners attempted to remove as little rock as possible as it was difficult and arduous work. Consequently these old workings were narrow and restrictive. St Thomas's Work is high up on the steep western flanks of Eel Crag and the copper ore extracted was hand dressed on site before being carried down to the valley floor on what is now a faint zig-zag grassy track.

Photo: *David Bridge*

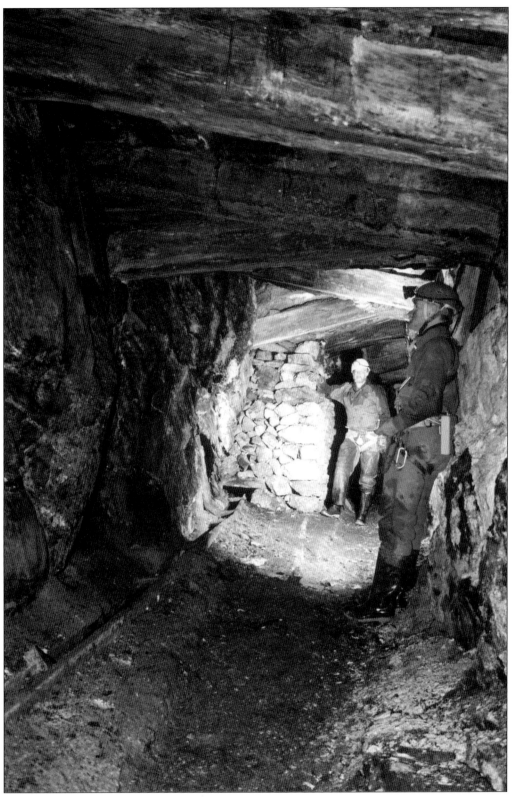

Modern day explorers re-enter a world created by the Victorian miners. This part of Deep Level in the Coniston Mine had not been entered since the miners departed over a hundred years ago. Nothing is disturbed or removed. Only photographs are taken.

Photo: *Max Dobie*

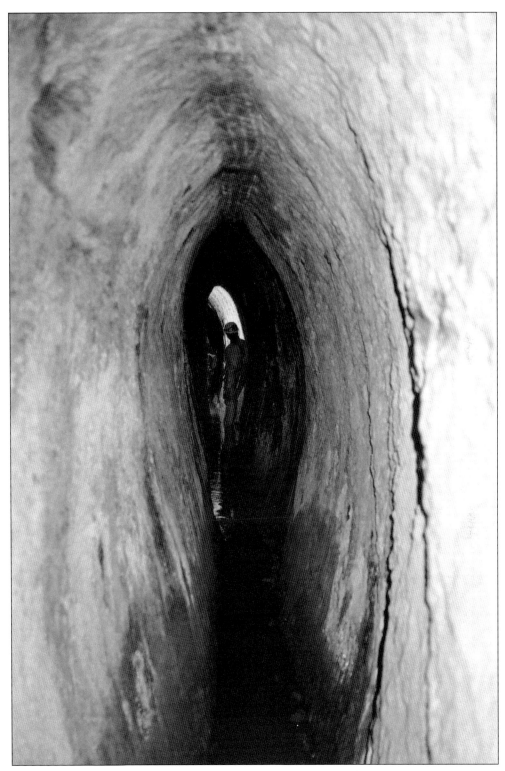

The beginnings of the Goldscope Mine are lost in the mists of antiquity. The mine had been working for at least 300 years when the Germans, under the leadership of Daniel Höchstetter, started to develop it in the 16th century. This photograph shows the finest example of a coffin level known in Lakeland. This tunnel was hand-driven through hard Skiddaw slate by the 16th century miners using only hammers, chisels, wedges and occasionally fire to help splinter the rock. The tunnel was used to carry water to an underground water wheel.

Photo: *Max Dobie*

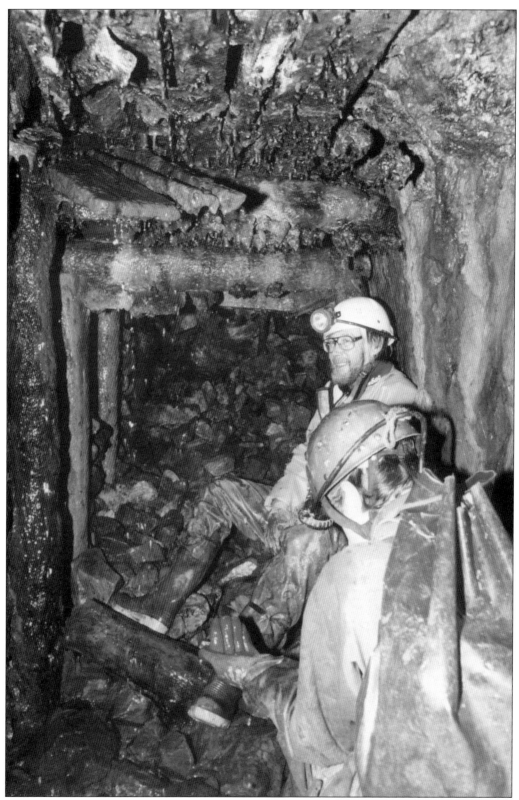

Within the Paddy End area of the Coniston Mine two explorers relax after an arduous descent. Exploring areas such as this was once the sport of potholers but has become, more recently, a serious task carried out by experienced and skilled mine-exploring archaeologists.

Photo: *Jon Knowles*

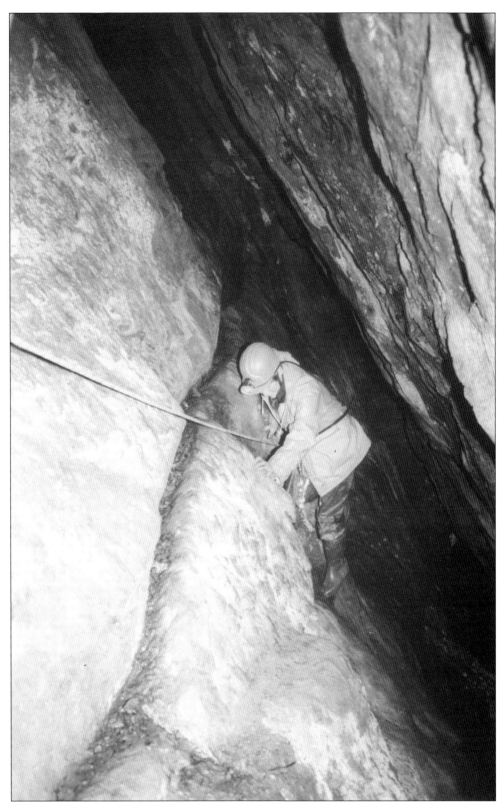

An explorer carefully picks her way down the footwall of a 'stope' within the Goldscope Mine. The channel in the footwall was a drainage channel cut by the Elizabethan miners to divert water away from the workings below and prevent accumulation at the bottom.

Photo: *Jon Knowles*

Within the Brow Stope area of the Coniston Copper Mines a miner's ladder rests where it was left over 100 years ago. Since work in this area of the Coniston Mine was abandoned secondary mineralisation has occurred and copper salts leaching from the rock walls display an intense blue where they have been deposited.

Photo: *Mike Mitchell*

From the opposite fellside the buildings of the Force Crag Mine, at the head of the Coledale Valley, stand out starkly against the spoil of centuries of mining. Force Crag was the last metalliferous mine to be worked in Lakeland. It was closed down in 1990 after a serious collapse in Zero Level, the main adit level, brought production to a halt.

Photo: *Peter Fleming*

137

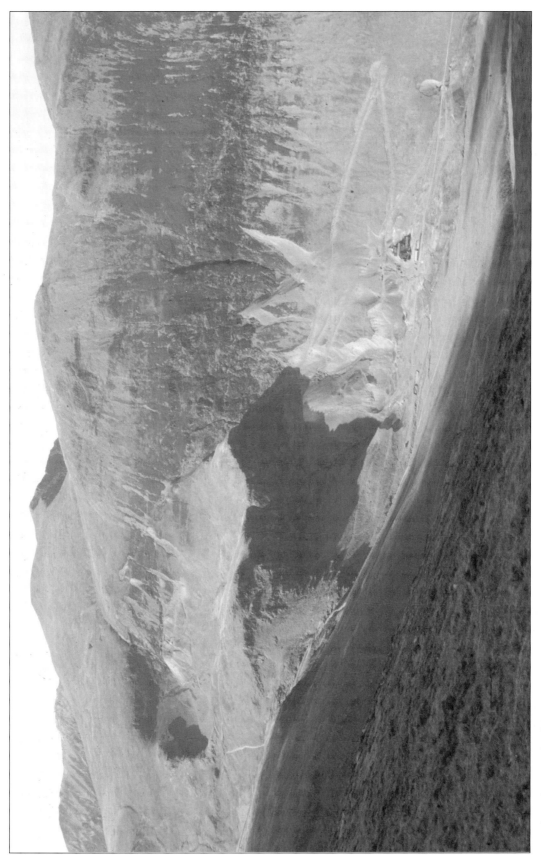

Another photograph of the Force Crag Mine shows the extent of workings up the shoulder of the mountain below and above the natural barrier of Force Crag (in shadow). The mill can be seen in the lower right hand portion of the photograph.

Photo: *Mike Mitchell*

During the late 1980s Force Crag Mine was worked on a part time basis, usually at weekends, by a group of skilled miners from the Cumbria area. This photograph shows one of the group taking the loco and train of trucks into Zero Level which was being developed as the main production level of the mine. It was a collapse a few meters in from the portal that eventually halted operations and closed for good the last ore mine in Lakeland.

Photo: *Ronnie Calvin*

The project at Force Crag Mine was not just concerned with developing Zero Level but also involved the re-commissioning of the old mill equipment on the surface. In this photograph ore from the hoppers beneath the 1500 Stope is filled into an ore tub by Peter Calvin, one of the Force Crag Miners. The ore was destined for commissioning trials in the mill. Watching is colleague Lindsay Greenbank.

Photo: *Ronnie Calvin*

A collapse on a barytes vein on the northern flank of High Pike. The rotten nature of the country rock is well illustrated in this picture. Also in evidence is the barytes vein itself. The vein has been removed to within three feet of the surface but the miners left a pillar of barytes about fifteen feet down.

Photo: *Alen McFadzean*

LAKELAND'S MINING HERITAGE – 'WAD'
by Dave Bridge

When a descent is made from Great Gable into Borrowdale by way of Brandreth and Grey Knotts, skirting the crags of Gillercomb and turning north-west down the long shoulder towards Seatoller, it is hard to imagine that beneath one's feet a famous Lake District mining industry was once in full swing. But near the place where Newhouse Gill drops steeply to join the River Derwent at Seathwaite the scene changes dramatically. Here the ground is pockmarked with shallow pits and cuttings, grassy mounds and ruined stone shelters. Spoil from more extensive workings leads down to the ancient boundary wall of Seatoller Common at the 1300 ft contour where a deep pit adds to the scarring of the landscape. Beyond the wall the fellside is pierced by a series of levels or 'stages'. A working of great depth lies half hidden beneath a camouflage of holly and more spoil is concealed in the small wood below.

Such intense activity in the volcanic heart of Lakeland may come as a surprise to the unsuspecting visitor. What rewards did the adventurers seek? What unheard of riches drove men to scratch and scrape at the turf and boulders to expose the bedrock beneath? If the winding miners' track is followed down the fellside a clue will be found in the form of a marker stone. This stone displays the inscription – 'John Bankes Esquier 1752'. The name Bankes is inseparable from the famous pencil industry of Keswick – and the mineral responsible for the founding of that industry was wad.

At least that is what the locals called it. To mineralogists wad is a dark earthy substance consisting mainly of hydrated manganese dioxide. But the Borrowdale wad is graphite, also called plumbago and earlier known as black-lead. These names disguise its true chemical nature which was determined in 1779 by the German scientist K W Scheele, though as late as 1825 Borrowdale wad was still being mistakenly called a 'carburet of iron'. Graphite in its pure form is carbon, less highly structured than diamond and composed of weakly bonded atomic layers. It is greasy to the touch which is due to tiny flakes or platelets rubbing off. These retain their crystalline structure and impart a metallic lustre to the deposit. Pure graphite can be machined, cut with a knife and sharpened to a point.

The working of graphite deposits is thought to have been well established by the mid 13th century in central Europe. By the 17th century deposits were being exploited in New England and the East Indies and possibly before that time in Spain and Mexico. Soon the occurrence of graphite in Siberia, Ceylon and many other places was known. Small deposits were worked in Scotland, e.g. Glen Strathfarrar, and in the Caldbeck Fells where a small graphite mine was opened in Bannerdale in the mid 19th century (in fact Bannerdale pencils are said to have been made). But nowhere else in the world have such large quantities of graphite of the purity of best Borrowdale wad been found.

For many years after its first discovery Borrowdale wad was used for marking sheep when it was also known as 'black cawke'. The development of best quality wad as a writing material from these early beginnings is of course well known, resulting in the high quality pencils of the 19ᵗʰ century. But its other uses have been as diverse as its many properties. It was used medicinally as early as 1693 and by 1709 was a recognised remedy for colic and for easing the pain of "gravel, the stone and strangury", when small quantities were ground up and taken in white wine or ale by country folk. As a lubricant it was exploited "for smoothing wood rollers and screws" such as on the rigging of ships, and its ability to endure high temperatures together with its resistance to thermal shock ensured a steady demand for the lower grade material in the manufacture of crucibles and other foundry ware. A combination of these properties made it valuable as a separating layer between iron moulds and castings, in fact it was said in 1752 to answer "this purpose better than any thing yet found out". Low grade wad was also much in demand for polishing and protecting ironware. An important overseas market developed mainly for pencil quality wad (e.g. 'crayons d'Angleterre') and it is even said to have been used in Holland in the glazing of earthenware pots.

Unlike other parts of the world where graphite occurs in metamorphosed rocks as bedded shales or as flakes disseminated throughout the country rock, in Borrowdale it is associated with an igneous intrusion. This fact was recorded by the 19ᵗʰ century geologist J Clifton Ward who also noted a system of veins associated with the deposit. The graphite is confined to a 400 metre stretch of the vein system and the richest finds appear to have occurred at the junction of the intrusion (described as diabase) with the Borrowdale Volcanics. The graphite occurs as lumps or nodules in pipes of anything up to 3 ft by 9 ft in cross-section and in sops or 'bellies' away from the veins, and was located by following

quartz strings which often contained thin graphite coatings. The random occurrence of the deposits and the numerous false leads made wad mining a frustrating affair particularly in later years when the surface outcrops had been worked out, a fact borne out by the labyrinthine nature of the workings.

There has been much argument over the origin of the Borrowdale graphite since it is not simply the result of the heating and restructuring of carbonaceous material within metamorphosed sedimentary rocks as many other graphite deposits are. In the absence of an immediate organic source the possibility of carbon from the decomposition of carbon monoxide, derived from the reduction of atmospheric carbon dioxide by minerals in the diabase, was put forward by Strens. However Firman pointed out that on this basis Borrowdale-type graphite should be very common. A theory first proposed by Professor Sedgwick in 1848 is that carbon from the underlying Skiddaw slates which contain the remains of minute forms of life from the seas of early Ordovician times (500 million years ago) was vapourised by later volcanic intrusions and re-deposited. Measurements of the isotopic ratio carbon 13/carbon 12 in samples of Borrowdale graphite reported in 1981 by Weis, Friedman and Gleason have given this early theory new impetus, but these workers propose that carbon monoxide from the reaction of superheated water vapour with the underlying carbon deposits rather than carbon vapour itself was the transport medium. In view of the low concentration of carbon available in the Skiddaw slates compared with the large volume of graphite in the Borrowdale vein system, which has always been a sticking point of this theory, Parnell suggests that the diabase acted as a channel for gases mobilised by other means implying an extended period for the build-up of the graphite. However from potassium-argon dating Mitchell and Ineson in 1975 came to the conclusion that the diabase intrusion and the graphite deposition both occurred at a similar geological time (i.e. late Caledonian or about 380 million years ago) and are therefore probably genetically connected. No doubt the arguments between geologists on the origin of this unique deposit will continue for many years to come.

Much of the mine's long history is clouded by folklore but since Postlethwaite's account of the workings several other attempts have been made to unravel the facts. William Camden's mention of "the famous mine of Wad or Black-lead", after his journey through the north of England in 1582 while researching for *Britannia*, was for many years thought to be the earliest written evidence of wad mining in Borrowdale. The exact time that the wad deposits were discovered however is obscure. It is likely that the Furness monks would have known of their existence because the manor of Borrowdale was in their possession until the dissolution of Furness Abbey by Henry VIII in 1537, but there are no known monastic records to support this view. On the premise that the monks would have put the wad to good use had they known of it, an imaginative attempt was recently made to search for evidence of graphite on the only surviving manuscript from Furness Abbey – two great folio volumes of the Coucher Book written by the monk John Stell in 1412. But a careful inspection of the rulings and guide lines drawn in to assist the scribe revealed nothing to suggest that good quality graphite was being extracted locally in the early 15th century, although it did appear that inferior iron-impregnated material, possibly stray pieces of wad picked up from the stream bed, had been in the monk's possession.

Nevertheless there is evidence to suggest that a wad mine had been established by the time of the Dissolution because according to Boon, the *Minister's Accounts* for the dissolved monastery of Furness dated 1540-41 include 6s 8d from the profit of a mine of stone called 'calkstone' otherwise 'Shepe Oodde' in Borrowdale, and the mine is again mentioned in 1542-44. Then in August 1555 a visit to the manor of Borrowdale by royal commissioners Thomas Legh and Nicholas Bardsey to enquire of ores etc, including any wad-hole "for the colouring or uring of shepe", resulted in the first recorded lease of the mineral rights for wad to one Ambrose Dormer of Oxfordshire.

It is interesting that the 1555 report refers only to the "Wad hole or Cauke pyt...lyeing in the Comon of Setower" (Seatoller). This is the upper working, later called Gorton's Pipe, which outcrops on the common above the boundary wall (where the deep pit now is) though it is possible that a second outcrop, Woodman's, was also being worked at the same wad hole. The report implies that the lower working or Grand Pipe some 120 yards down the slope in enclosed ground had not yet been discovered. A long held belief that wad was first discovered below a large uprooted ash (or oak) tree in Queen Elizabeth's time (i.e. 1558 or after) almost certainly refers to the later discovery.

By 1565 the Company of Mines Royal had set up their copper mining industry at Keswick and German miners were beginning to arrive in the district bringing their expertise in both mining and smelting techniques. According to the 1555 report the wad mine was badly in need of such mining skills "the said wad beyng very dangerus to get by reason of habundance of waters..." and on the face of it one might expect Daniel Höchstetter, the manager of operations at Keswick, to have taken an active interest in the Borrowdale wad. The Keswick mining company's terms of reference were however carefully spelled out in letters patent which granted the mining only of gold, silver, copper and quicksilver and an indenture which extended this to tin, lead, precious stones and pearl, and there is no indication in the account books of the German miners up to 1577 nor in any existing inventories or reports up to 1602 that any interaction occurred between the two mining concerns, not even the use of Borrowdale graphite for crucibles in the Keswick smelthouse. It was not until 1607 that a link was forged and the wad holes were sub-let to the brothers Emanuel and Daniel Höchstetter (jnr) who had taken over the running of the Keswick industry at their father's death in 1581.

There are good reasons to believe that the market for wad was opening up towards the end of the 16th century even though this is not reflected in the yearly rent paid to the Crown which stood at 13s 4d from 1555 until after 1614. By 1594, when a certain Matthew Buck took over the lease, both upper and lower wad holes were being worked, and although a lawsuit of 1597 specifically refers to the upper being officially confined to use by manorial tenants for "the markinge or smutting of their sheepe and other their necessary use" and "not to sell the same or dispose of it in any other sort..." there was no such restriction on the lower wad hole. Furthermore the case reveals that seven tons of superior wad worth over £13 per ton had been stored in a barn at Seathwaite, presumably awaiting shipment elsewhere.

The earliest known description of a pencil, that by Gesner of Zurich in 1565, refers to the use of "a kind of lead...others call it English antimony" and Camden in 1582 described wad as a stone "which painters use to draw their lines and make pictures of one colour in their first draughts...". There is also evidence that Flemish traders were supplying the Michelangelo School of Art in Italy with Cumberland graphite by about 1580 and by 1602 the Company of Merchant Adventurers of Newcastle-upon-Tyne had deemed it necessary to add black-lead to their levy lists.

So by the time the Germans took over it is likely that work at the lower wad hole would have been well advanced. By 1620 they were driving an adit to drain this work to a depth of 100 ft and although now collapsed at the portal the so-called Old Men's Stage can still be inspected by descending the Grand Pipe. The coffin shaped outline of this level and adjacent side workings and also the telltale grooves which are characteristic of stope (wedge) and feather work clearly illustrate German handiwork and we have documentary evidence to confirm this. For example, parish records show that Thomas Kalcher left Coniston for Seathwaite some time between 1610 and 1612, the year that his fourth child William was baptised. He originally came from Newlands and would have carried with him the skills and knowledge of Steffan Kalcher, an experienced pickman who had worked at the Goldscope mine in the latter part of the 16th century and was buried in Newlands in 1594. By the year 1602 English miners at Coniston had been taught the skill of working hard rock by their German colleagues so it is likely that pickmen of English stock were also involved in the drainage work at this time. Another skill which the Germans are thought to have brought to the wad mines was that of hushing or 'damage', i.e. washing away the surface soil to examine the rock beneath for veins and surface outcrops. This practice was not new to the district. For instance only a few years earlier visiting Crown inspectors had recommended to the Company of Mines Royal that at the Caldbeck mines "it were meet that one or more dams were made to discover the Veins at the topp...".

In 1613 ownership of the wad mine changed when James I granted lands in the manor of Borrowdale to Londoners Whitmore and Vernon. They immediately sold off each of the tenancies to its occupier under the terms of the Great Deed of Borrowdale, one copy of which is dated 28 November 1614, but the wad holes were the subject of a separate transaction and became the property of local gentlemen William Lamplugh and Charles Hudson. The Höchstetter mining rights were unaffected by these transactions, but Emanuel died in 1614 and in 1625 part of the lease was bought by the London lawyer Sir John Bankes, son of John Bankes a wealthy Keswick tradesman. Sir John, whose residence was Corfe Castle in Dorset, had three years earlier purchased the Lamplugh share or moiety in the mine with his father-in-law Ralph Hawtrey. And so in the year 1625 the Bankes family began to work the wad mine, an association which was to last for over two centuries. But the Höchstetters still retained an interest. Daniel's son Francis and Emanuel's son Joseph had now become partners in the enterprise and furthermore the marriage of Joseph to Sir John's sister Joyce before her death in 1622 had forged a family connection with the Bankes.

Though the copper industry suffered badly from the Civil War the supply of Borrowdale wad was unaffected. The nature of the deposits, i.e. lumps or nodules generally varying in weight from less than 1 oz to 6 or 7 lbs and occasionally upwards of 50 lbs, which could easily be removed by hand from the pipes and sops and required no treatment other than washing and sorting, meant that once a rich deposit had been discovered many tons could be extracted in a short time with little expense and the market flooded. For instance after a large find in the 1760s seven tons of wad worth about £3000 were extracted in forty-eight hours and a workman once affirmed that he could "get the value of £1000 in half an hour". For this reason sale agreements at the time included a condition whereby to maintain the re-sale value the proprietors undertook not to open the mine again within an agreed period or a penalty would be imposed by the purchaser (in later years the proprietors themselves controlled the supply and continued the practice of periodic opening). A series of such bargains between the mine owners and London or Newcastle merchants during the period 1646 to 1671 each involved about seventy tons of wad with mine closure clauses of six or seven years. This wad was sold in different grades from pieces "the bigness of a hen's egg" down to pieces "the bigness of a White pea", and later in the period "the rock or fourth sort" and an even more inferior fifth sort. Over the twenty-five years the price per ton of the best grade material increased from £18 to £100.

By 1710 the mine was owned jointly by the Shepheard and Bankes families, a partnership that was to last for half a century, and in that year the Old Men's Stage was reopened after a period of 32 years during which time there had been no official inspection of the old workings. It is not difficult to imagine the eager anticipation of the mine officials as they entered the narrow winding level, and their colourful use of the vernacular when it was revealed that thieves had been in before them and "carried on the old work, till they had lost it in the rock". Thankfully a rich new 'belly' was soon discovered back from the forehead. The temporary abandonment of the lower workings does not imply that the mine had been unproductive in the latter part of the 17th century – a view popularly held. By 1690 the French possessed a navy of over two-hundred ships and the English and Dutch were endeavouring to reaffirm their command of the sea. It is known that the demand on graphite for facing the inside of cannon ball moulds was restricting supplies for pencils at that time and to close the mine completely would hardly make sense. Furthermore Thomas Robinson wrote in 1709 that "the vein is opened but once in seven years" which was normal practice, and there were many rich deposits still to be found in the upper wad hole.

Also in the year 1710 Bishop Nicolson of Carlisle, a notable scholar and historian who five years earlier had been granted a Fellow of the Royal Society by its president Sir Isaac Newton, made the journey to Seathwaite to visit the mine and was "courteously received" by John Shepheard. The bishop took the trouble to record his observations yet it was to be another forty years before a vivid description in the *Gentleman's Magazine* attracted the attention of a wider public. After that the wad mine became the focal point of a long procession of tourists including the poet Thomas Gray, the travel writer William Gilpin, Captain Budworth and many others. In 1765 the French mining engineer Gabriel Jars included the mine in

his *Voyages Metallurgiques* and the chemist and mineralogist Charles Hatchett in his 1796 tour of England and Scotland when visiting "mines and manufactories". Many of these left valuable eye-witness accounts.

To maintain output development work was necessary and over the years more levels were driven into the fellside. These served several purposes – exploration (by following veins or strings), drainage, ventilation and tramway access to the various deposits. Exploratory levels, notably Common and Moor stages which produced a little wad, were eventually driven on Seatoller Common beyond the boundary wall and a low trial was made into the side of the gill but the main upper deposits were worked at different times from the day levels known as Gorton's Stage, Harrison's Stage and finally Gill Stage. By the time a connection had been made with the lower workings through Grisdale's Pipe, two further day levels had been opened below including Fairey's Stage which served the productive middle part of the mine. In the years 1735-36 the upper stage was extended by the Gorton brothers who may well have been related to the Swaledale mining family of that name, as James Gorton, a miner of Gunnerside, had become a leaseholder of the Tilberthwaite copper mines in 1717. Gunpowder was in use by then but it is quite possible that a much earlier attempt had already been made by hand to drain the upper wad hole.

Around this time the agent or 'steward' would be Thomas Dixon, the first of a long line of Dixons associated with the mine whose integrity and ability were much valued; "for more than fifty years he has given the most perfect satisfaction to the proprietors" was written of one of his descendants. One of his main responsibilities would be the mine's security as the stealing of wad was a perennial problem and best quality wad was soon to fetch 12s per pound or over £1300 per ton. For that reason a security lodge was built at the entrance to the upper workings where dwelt an armed guard day and night to keep an eye on the site, and when the mine was opened in the 1760s the eight workmen employed there were closely watched by six overseers who frequently searched their pockets for wad. During periods of inactivity all openings were filled with waste and the precaution was taken of throwing to the bottom any poor quality wad which had not been extracted. Such caches can still be found today. The lodge situated just below the boundary wall was an elaborate affair and contained at least three rooms with a roadway passing through the building to the portal of Harrison's Stage. A smaller building had been erected over the entrance to the Old Men's Stage and it became the practice during periods of closure to further protect the entrances by temporary masonry work and walling within. However, pilfering of the spoil heaps was rife and could provide a comfortable subsistence for the pickers who "digging with mattocks, and other instruments" could generally clear six or eight shillings a day and sometimes more – up to ten times the wage of a farm worker or quarryman.

From a scene of clandestine operations and illicit dealings colourful characters emerge. Less well-known perhaps than the legendary smuggler Black Sal is William Hetherington who made an ambitious and successful attempt to work the wad mine from across Newhouse Gill (then known as Wadhole Gill) where in about 1740 he opened a small copper level. In the timber lining of his modest working a secret door gave access to a branch which ran direct to the wad beneath his neighbour's land. He was luckier than Black Sal (who was allegedly hunted to her death by wolfhounds) and his misdemeanour landed him the job of a steward at the wad mine. A narrow level can be found amongst the rocks and bracken across the gill but if this were Hetherington's working a heavy roof fall has obliterated any evidence of his lucrative little enterprise.

And lucrative it could be, for one "gang of villains" was accustomed to stealing wad worth £1000 per year – equivalent to well over £100,000 today. Greed proved to be their downfall one January night in 1751 when they attacked the lodge at the upper mine with fire arms "but losing one of their number by the fire from the place, the rest fled". The increasing boldness of such raids and the never ending pilfering spurred the proprietors into action. A petition to Parliament followed by a Bill guided through by John Bankes' brother Henry, who being true to the family tradition was then a Tory MP for the borough of Corfe, resulted in the much quoted 1752 Act of George II whereby stealing and receiving wad would be treated as felony and thus punishable by public whipping and a year's imprisonment with hard labour, or by up to seven years' transportation. The recent Jacobite rebellion and the mounting colonial rivalry between Britain and France at the time no doubt worked in the proprietors' favour and gave the Bill a degree of urgency as the wad was still needed for the "casting of bomb-shells, round-shot and canon-balls". As a further precaution John Bankes called a halt to local sales of wad. But these deterrents and the placing of marker stones about the site had little long term effect. Even as consignments of wad left the Seathwaite guard house for Kendal under armed escort on the first stage of their journey to London lively black market trading between miners and foreign dealers was under way at The Bunch of Grapes (now The George Hotel) in Keswick, and the routes to the coast must have been as diverse as the smugglers were devious – as illustrated by a recent find of best wad in the Grisedale Pike area. The wad pickers were equally busy, for on a winter's night the flicker of as many as 40 lanterns could be seen up on Seatoller Fell. According to Shelagh Sutton a shot from William Dixon's blunderbuss would "mak em run like clipt hens". In 1930 there was still a blunderbuss lying around at Seathwaite farm.

From 1750 to 1769 the lower working remained closed and in about 1760, according to Gabriel Jars, a new large deposit yielding £3000 worth of wad was discovered in the upper mine. The moiety of the wad mines belonging to the Shepheard family had in February 1758 been let to "several gentlemen, chiefly residing in London" who must have viewed this find with some satisfaction. When the Old Men's Stage was eventually re-opened with the intention of re-working the Grand Pipe the latter became so unmanageable due to its great depth – about 200 feet below adit – that the work finally had to be abandoned; but not before Wickersley's Sop had been discovered behind a rider in one of the veins yielding 177 casks of the best wad and nine years later the "Great Opening" Sop yielding 417 casks containing 70 lbs each which would be worth at least £43,000 as wad was by now fetching up to 30s per pound.

The poor quality wad from Wickersley's Sop was initially stowed on or behind bunnings in the Grand Pipe but in 1778 it was ground down to a coarse powder and thrown into the beck – a novel way of cheating the thieves. There were two more workings of existing deposits up to 1788 but after that date the prospects began to look bleak. Apart from a five ton deposit of low grade wad nothing of any size was discovered for some years and although the company had a large stock in reserve a great deal of dead work was carried out. In 1793 Captain Budworth noted "now they are afraid the mine is exhausted" and when Charles Hatchett visited the mine in 1796 he found seven men employed and a new exploratory level being driven from surface. At that time the Bankes moiety was owned by a Henry Bankes and one of the eight shareholders of the old Shepheard moiety was Sir Joseph Bankes, a mining entrepreneur who greatly admired Hatchett's scientific abilities.

In 1793 Parliament voted overwhelmingly for a redoubling of British naval and military effort in the build-up to the Napoleonic Wars but by that time munitions work would have had little if any impact on the demand for graphite because in 1758 the ironmaster Isaac Wilkinson (previously of Backbarrow) had taken out a patent for "A new method or invention for casting of Guns or Cannon...in dry sand", claiming that they would be "made and cast in a much more neat, complete, exact and useful, as well as cheap and expeditious manner than any method hitherto known and made use of". However the cottage industry of pencil-making was quietly exerting increasing pressure on the dwindling supply of best wad, now at the inflated price of 3 gns per pound and still rising. Already John Ladyman who left the woollen industry to make pencils soon after the year 1800 was involved with the mine. Now under considerable pressure the proprietors at last decided to drive a much needed adit about 200 feet below the Old

Men's Stage and this, Gilbert's Stage, was begun in 1798. The work can be inspected today and the quantity of spoil alone shows that the 220 yards to the Grand Pipe was no small undertaking, for example it was to be twenty-seven years before a project of similar magnitude was carried out at the Coniston Copper Mine when John Taylor began his Deep Level adit to the Bonsor Vein.

In 1800 the lower part of the Grand Pipe was at last de-watered. This development heralded a new phase in the mine's working methods because internal connections eventually enabled wad from different parts of the mine to be trammed out by this new route. A substantial building was constructed at the entrance with a room where the workers changed their clothes under the eyes of a resident security guard and three years later the efforts were rewarded with the discovery of a very large deposit of wad, Dixon's Pipe, which surprisingly had eluded the miners until now. This was found beyond the Grand Pipe "after a tedious search" and yielded 500 casks of the best wad containing about 140 lbs each. According to Postlethwaite working costs for 1803 amounted to a mere four percent of the profit for that year but it must be remembered that a considerable amount of dead work had already been carried out. Today the dripping cavity of Dixon's Pipe over 150 ft deep lies empty and threatening far within the mine and clearly its working would have been severely handicapped without the drainage, ventilation and tramming capability provided by Gilbert's Stage. Nothing of quite this magnitude was ever found again, although there were further significant discoveries including Winkle's Pipe at the junction of two veins in 1812 which yielded 87 casks of the best wad, now at 35s per pound, and a considerable amount of inferior wad.

These discoveries must have been a great relief to all concerned. By now the Keswick pencil makers were beginning to set up factories, including Jacob Banks, but it is ironic that by the time the pencil firm of Banks and Co was established at Forge Mill in 1832 the wad mines were on the decline. According to Otley the price of best wad stood at 45s per pound in 1833 when a few casks were filled. To speed up exploration work it had become the practice to employ more hands and open the mine more frequently or for longer periods. Since the discovery of Winkle's Pipe a few encouraging deposits had been found including Grisdale's Pipe but there was nothing to match the earlier bonanzas. And now the fortunes of the wad mine were further dampened by a backlash from the Napoleonic Wars. In 1794 after trade between Britain and France had ceased and the French were unable to obtain graphite of pencil quality a French inventor named Nicholas-Jacques Conté, was commissioned to develop substitute pencil 'leads' by mixing powdered graphite with powdered clay. The experiment was a great success allowing pencils of different hardnesses to be manufactured. From about the mid-1830s the pencil industry turned more and more to composite graphite of this type and the demand for the pure wad diminished, although a stock was kept for the very best pencils.

From the late 1830s the mine was let to a series of companies and by 1850 a lower trial level, Robson's, had been driven on Rake Vein for some years and a cross cut had intersected Hasting's Pipe which had been worked to 100 ft below Gilbert's Stage but was water-logged. In 1859 John Dixon was convinced there were "many sops or bodies of wad yet undiscovered" but apart from a possible isolated find in 1875 his hopes were never realised and when the last of the companies went into liquidation in 1891 the mines were abandoned for good.

Towards the end of the century the pencil works were still drawing on their stocks of best wad but by 1906 foreign imports had completely taken over and sadly the story of Borrowdale wad came to an end.

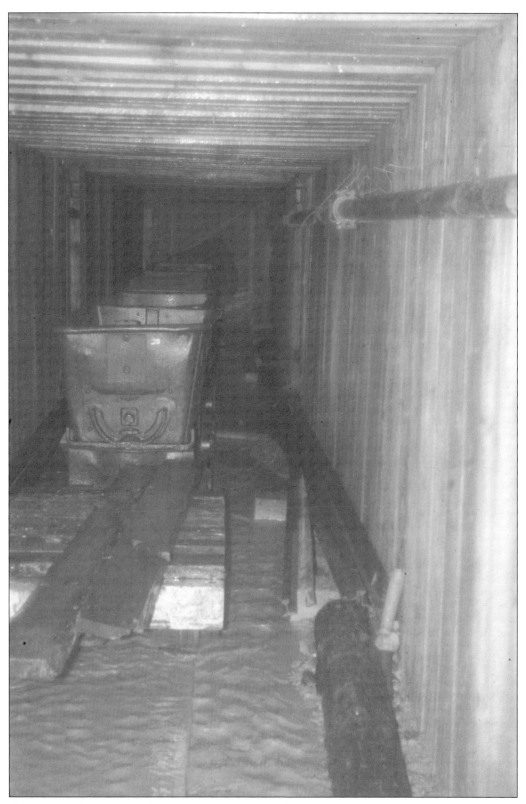

Just within the portal of Zero Level at Force Crag Mine a train of ore tubs waits on the tracks beneath the timber shuttering. This photograph was taken in 1989 a few months before the shuttering collapsed creating a blockage that rapidly flooded Zero Level to the roof and closed the mine completely.

Photo: *Ian Matheson*

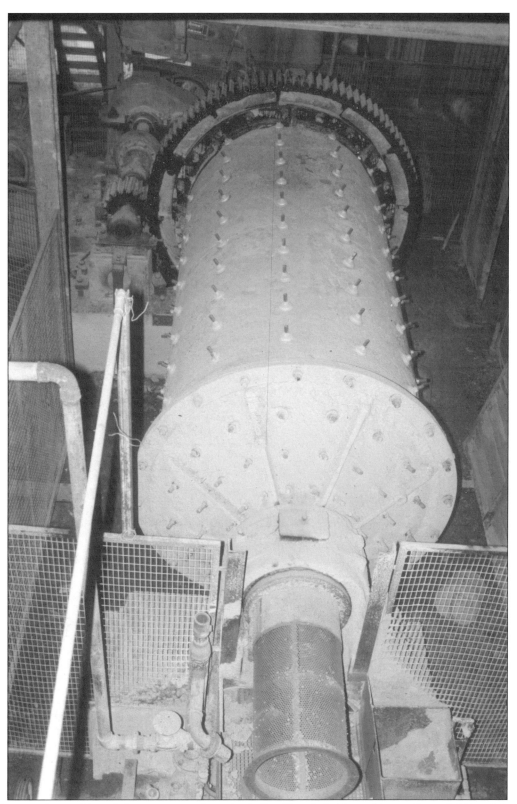

The photographs on this and the next page show the ball mill and shaking tables at Carrock Mine, Mosedale, installed within the mine buildings in the 1970s to separate and concentrate ore. The machinery has since been removed and the buildings demolished.

Photos: *Ian Matheson*

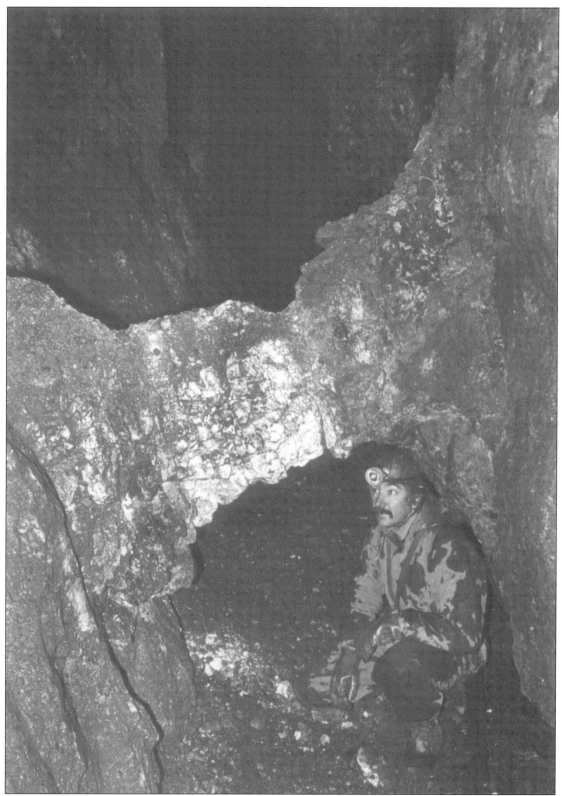

A barytes pillar in the Blockley Vein, Potts Gill Mine. This particular pillar is small compared with examples in High Force and areas of the Caldbeck Fells. Pillars were left in situ to prevent the walls of the worked-out veins buckling under pressure and collapsing into the mine.

Photo: *Alen McFadzean*

Built in 1940 in a high and exposed location, the compressor cabin still stands next to the entrance of the High Force Cross Cut on the flank of Grisedale Pike. The entrance is at an altitude of 1700ft where working was often hampered by ice and snow. During the severe winter of 1947 the mine was cut off for 6 weeks. Eventually flooding and damage forced the mine to close.

Photo: *Ian Matheson*

Driggith Mine began as a lead mine in the late 18th century and as late as 1948 attempts were still being made to re-work the old stopes in the 30 fathom level, this time for barytes. The old workings and dressing plant are situated near the head of Driggith Beck in the Caldbeck Fells but little of the plant remains today.

Photo: *David Bridge*

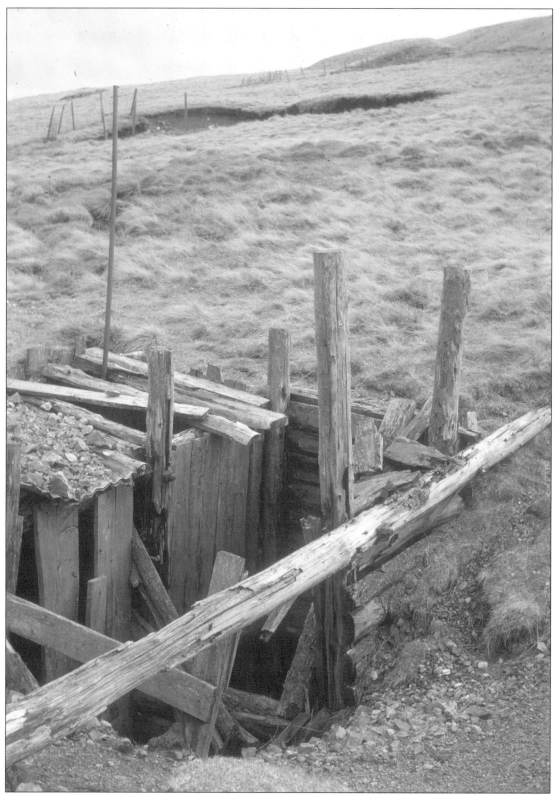

Abandonment in the fells above Potts Gill, Caldbeck. Here, a shaft from one of the Potts Gill workings stands derelict and dangerous. The shaft has since collapsed. All dangerous subsidence craters and open shafts in the Caldbeck fells are now securely fenced.

Photo: *Dave Bridge*

LAKELAND'S MINING HERITAGE – LEAD & ZINC
by Ian Matheson and Chris Jones

Lead was one of the first metals to be discovered, and has been in use for at least 8000 years. It is a soft metal, which is easy to work and does not corrode. Its main ore, galena, occurs widely, and can be smelted at temperatures which can be reached in an ordinary campfire.

The earliest known example is a necklace of lead beads found at Catal Huyuk in Anatolia. Much later it was used by the Romans to make water pipes and cisterns, and as a roofing material. When the Romans left Britain civilisation declined, and so too did the need for minerals and mining skills. Throughout mediaeval times relatively small amounts of lead were used for roofing churches and other buildings, and it was not until the 16th century that a boom in the building of great houses brought about an increased demand for lead for roofs and guttering. In the 18th and 19th centuries Britain was the world's largest producer, and many new uses were found for the metal. It was used in lead-based paints and lead crystal glass, as well as for making bullets and lead shot. In the 20th century demand increased further as lead was used for electrical cables and batteries, and as an additive in petrol, but in Britain lead mining declined as cheaper lead was imported from Spain, Australia and the USA. The last British lead mines finally closed in the 1960s.

The most important ore of lead is the sulphide, known as galena, which contains about 86% lead, and is a brittle, heavy, silver-grey mineral which forms cubic crystals. It is usually found in fissures resulting from faults and joints in limestone and in veins and pockets in volcanic rocks. It occurs in strings of quartz, fluorspar, calcite or barytes, is often associated with zinc and copper, and usually contains a small proportion of silver which can add to its value. The gangue material forms much the greater part of the content of a vein and used to be regarded as waste. Now materials such as barytes and fluorspar are often the more important products and the metal ores are regarded as a by-product.

Zinc is often found in association with lead. The most common ore is sphalerite, known as blende or black jack. It is used to make dry cell batteries, as an additive in paints and for galvanising iron to prevent rusting. In the early days it was a waste material, and being of a similar density to galena there was difficulty in separating the ores.

The simplest method of concentrating ore was by gravity. It was first crushed to a powder by bucking with hammers, or by using stamps or crushing rollers, and then processed in water. Jigging was the method by which the fine ore was agitated in tanks of water so that the heavier metal particles settled to the bottom and the lighter rock particles were left on the top and could be skimmed off. Buddling involved washing ore in a fine stream of water when the lighter particles were carried further, and so separated from the heavier metal. These techniques were not effective in separating galena, sphalerite and barytes, which have similar densities, and it was not until 1898 that the Elmore Flotation Process made this possible. This used the affinity of sulphides for certain oils, which could then be floated off in water. Later, gas bubbles were used to enhance this process.

In the Lake District zinc was produced mainly at the mines of Force Crag, Threlkeld and Thornthwaite. Lead was found in many places but the principal mining fields were in the Helvellyn, Newlands and Caldbeck areas.

There are no records or remains of very early mining in the Lake District, and whilst it is probable that the metal was extracted from pre-Roman times, any traces which might have been left have long since been obliterated by later workings. As new mining and smelting techniques have been developed it has often been thought worthwhile to re-open old workings which had been abandoned as no longer viable, and to re-process old waste heaps. This re-working of old mining fields results in the destruction of the older remains and wipes the record clean. Most of the remains which are now visible date from the 19th and 20th centuries.

There are few records for the centuries after the Romans left, and although there are references in mediaeval documents pertaining to land grants relating to lead mining, there are few detailed records dating from earlier than the 16th century. At that time the Crown took an interest in mineral resources and in 1564 the Company of Mines Royal was formed. There were twenty-four shares, eleven of which were initially owned by the Augsburg firm of Haug, Langnaur & Co, and royalties were payable to Queen Elizabeth I. Their principal interest was in copper, which was mined at Keswick and at Coniston, and experienced miners, known as 'Dutchmen', were imported from Germany to carry out the work. Lead was required for separating the silver from copper ore but apparently none was available locally, for this was imported from Alston Moor, indicating that there were no local lead mines producing at that time. The Elizabethans eventually operated lead mines in the Derwent area at Stoneycroft, Brandlehow, Barrow and Thornthwaite, and in the Caldbeck Fells at Red Gill and Roughtongill. In 1564 a lead mine was opened in Greenhead Gill at Grasmere, but this venture was not successful and the mine closed in 1573. It was never re-opened and the remains that can still be seen are well worth a visit. They are said to be truly Elizabethan, but careful examination suggests that at least some of the remains have been re-built or re-worked at a much later date. (This is dealt with in detail in an article in *The Mine Explorer, Vol 4*, entitled 'The Elizabethan Lead Mine at Greenhead Gill'). At the same time Goldscope Mine, in German 'Gottes Gab', meaning God's Gift, was successfully worked for copper, but it was not until 1852 that lead was discovered there and became the principal ore to be extracted at that mine.

The Company of Mines Royal was not profitable. Between 1564 and 1600 metals to the value of £68,103 had been sold, but £104,709 had been expended. The Civil War contributed to an unfavourable economic climate, and it is said that in 1661 Cromwell's troops destroyed the smelter at Brigham, near Keswick, and enlisted some of the miners. Mining in the Lake District was therefore in decline during much of the 17th century, and it was not until the end of that century that mining resumed on any substantial scale. It would appear that another party of 'Dutchmen' came to the district in 1690, and lead was mined at Hartsop, near Brotherswater, on the side of Barrow, near Derwentwater, and nearby in Stoneycroft Gill, where a smelter was also constructed. An early mining disaster took place here, for in order to sink a shaft in the bed of the gill the stream had been diverted and a dam built. Without warning the dam burst and the water cascading down the gill flooded the shaft, drowning the men below and burying them in sand. It is said that their bodies were never recovered.

Water was always a problem for miners, but never more so than in the early days. It had to be lifted from the workings by bucket or by hand pump. Work often had to cease during winter months. A letter written by mining engineer David Davies, about 1690, relating to Barrow Mine, contained several references to the water being too strong. A level, 300 fathoms in length, was driven under the sole of the work to clear the water, and wrought night and day for seven years. When they came to clear the water they found that "the ore did not continue two fathoms deeper"! Lead mining was also carried on at Greenside during this period, and may have been started as early as 1650 near the summit of the mountain, where the ore outcropped at the surface. Dressed ore was taken by packhorse over Sticks Pass to the smelter at Stoneycroft, a distance of ten miles up hill and down dale.

Progress in mining is intermittent, for success depends on many factors. Luck, demand, a suitable economic climate, the availability of capital and improvements in technology all play their part, so few mines have been worked continuously for long periods. During the 18th century iron mining flourished, and there was some mining of copper for a time, but there is no record of great or continuous activity in the Lake District so far as lead mining was concerned. Various people worked the mines at Barrow, and Thornthwaite Mine was worked in the 18th century. Smelters were operated at Roughtongill and at Hartsop, but lead extraction in the North West in the 18th century was largely the work of the London Lead Company at Alston Moor. Some lead mines in Patterdale were worked about 1750, but it is not known for how long. Top Level at Greenside was driven in 1790, some 40

fathoms below the summit, and stoped out to the surface, but the mine was then abandoned for several years. Shortly after 1800 plans were made to re-establish the mine, leading in 1822 to the formation of the Greenside Mining Company. This mine was to become the richest in the area, and was to be worked more or less continuously for the next 150 years, though not without some setbacks and changes of ownership.

Some 2,400,000 tons of lead ore were produced during the life of the mine, and 2,000,000 ounces of silver. In the early days the dressed ore was taken elsewhere to be smelted, firstly to Stoneycroft Gill, and then, from 1820, to Alston where the London Lead Company had erected an up-to-date smelter. During the 1830s a smelter was built at the foot of Lucy Tongue Gill, and a flue arched with stone was cut out of the bedrock, ending a mile away on the Stang, where there was a stack. The course of this flue can easily be traced today, and part of the stack is still standing. This smelter was in operation until the beginning of the 20th century, when it was decided to close it, and to send the dressed ore by train from Troutbeck to Newcastle on Tyne for processing.

By 1850 the upper part of the mine was worked out, and the Willie Shaft was begun from Low Horse Level. At the same time the Lucy Tongue Adit was started. Its entrance was located just above the smelt mill, 82 fathoms below Low Horse Level. Working in three shifts, 24 hours a day, this took sixteen years to complete, and followed a circuitous course to take advantage of a soft vein. Even with two men per shift hand boring, they were not able to cut more than 120 yards a year.

Greenside Mine was one of the most valuable in the North of England, but it is unique because it was the first mine in Britain to use electrical winding and underground haulage, generating its own electricity by means of water turbines. Formerly, power was provided by two turbines and several water wheels, and by two underground hydraulic engines. The old upper levels of the mine were bricked up and used to store water for these turbines.

The Victorian pipework and the breached internal dams are still in place, as are seven-hundred feet of miner's ladders descending from Glencoyne Level almost to Lucy Tongue, which were subsequently put in to provide an alternative escape route from the mine.

In 1890 William Borlase became manager, and he persuaded the Company to modernise and to install a hydro-electric plant. Water was brought from dams built at Red Tarn and Keppel Cove Tarn, two miles distant from the mine, and conveyed in a partly-covered flume which follows the contour at the foot of Catstycam for well over a mile. This discharged into a 15" pipe, giving a fall of 420 feet to a 'Y piece' which directed the water through a vortex turbine and a pelton wheel, powering two 100 hp dynamos. The electricity was taken into the mine via the Lucy Tongue Level. The vortex turbine and generator provided the power for a 50 hp winding motor at the head of Smith's Shaft, situated underground two miles away from the generating station, and for a 14 hp electric locomotive working in the Lucy Tongue and hauling out to 'day' over a distance of one and a half miles. The pelton wheel provided electrical power for a 50 hp motor driving a compressor and for two 10 hp motors driving pumps on the 60 and 90 fathom levels. All the lighting, both underground and in the mill and office buildings, was supplied from the main generating station. The capacity of this plant was increased over the years as demand grew, and it operated until 1936 when the National Grid was brought in. Extensive remains can still be seen of the system of dams and leats which gathered every available drop of water from the mountainsides.

Twice there were serious floods caused by the breaching of the dams. The first was in 1870 when a great storm partially burst Top Dam up towards Sticks Pass. Water flooding down Lucy Tongue Gill carried away part of the silver refining building, and it is said that a hundred-ounce plate of silver went with it and was never recovered. The second was when the earth dam at Keppel Cove was breached. High on the slopes of Helvellyn the tarn, which remains dry to this day, once covered an area of six acres, and was contained by an earth dam forty feet high and a hundred feet thick at its base. During the night of 29th October 1927 a hole fifty feet wide was torn in the dam, and the tarn emptied itself down the valley towards Glenridding, two and a half miles away. Much damage was done but, amazingly, there was no loss of life. This disaster nearly closed the mine, as the Company paid heavy compensation, but new capital was found and the mine continued to work until 1934 when the low price of lead stopped operations.

In 1936 it was taken over by the Basinghall Mining Syndicate who carried out much redevelopment, and the mine became profitable once more. By the end of the war, however, the workings had bottomed out into the Skiddaw slate, and it was apparent that the ore reserves were becoming exhausted. Despite a programme of exploration started in 1947 to find new deposits, no ore was found and the mine moved towards its final closure, which took place in 1962.

Both before and since the closure there have been attempts at landscaping, and some of the buildings have been demolished whilst others were converted to bothies and to a Youth Hostel. Much of the land has been acquired by the National Park and the National Trust. The bare bones of the mine remain, and there are miles of old leats contouring the fell side from the dams at Red Tarn, Brown Cove, Keppel Cove, High Dam and Glencoyne. The Lucy Tongue Level was blown in, but water still drained from the rubble; the smelter flue traverses the hillside, and there is much of interest to be seen in and above Lucy Tongue Gill. For many years the only way to reach the Lucy Tongue Level was via the Glencoyne Adit and a 700 foot descent down the old ladder-way, requiring great care. Mine explorers obtained permission to re-open the Lucy Tongue Level and early in 1997, after three years of hard labour and considerable expense, succeeded in clearing a way through. Gates have been installed by the Cumbria Amenity Trust Mining History Society at both the Glencoyne and the Lucy Tongue entrances. These are securely locked, and there is no access to the general public.

Elsewhere in the Lake District not much remains of the lead mines at Thornthwaite and Barrow, nor of those in the Caldbeck Fells. There are workings at Hartsop and Eagle Crag which are worth examining, whilst at Wythburn Mine as well as underground workings, the old self-acting incline and drum house can still be seen. Goldscope in the Newlands Valley was mined for copper by the Elizabethans, but in 1852 the copper adit reached the lead vein, and some 5000 tons of lead ore was raised over the next twenty years. The lead vein is no longer accessible however and the interesting remains at Goldscope are those of Elizabethan copper workings, which have been modified in some places by 19th century miners.

The last mine to work in the Lake District National Park was Force Crag, which has had a long and varied history. It is thought that there may have been some activity in Elizabethan times, but there was no work of any consequence until the early years of the 19th century. Several leases were taken out, but it was not until 1840 that any quantity of ore was produced, and between then and 1865 some 590 tons of lead and 1300 ounces of silver were sold; the ore being carted to Maryport and then shipped to Liverpool. The coming of the Keswick to Penrith Railway, reaching Braithwaite in 1865, would have simplified this operation, but falling lead prices caused the mine to become unprofitable and it closed in that year. Two years later another company was formed to re-open the mine, this time to extract barytes, and after renovating the mine, which had become derelict after two years of closure, they were quickly into production. Transportation became much more organised, and ore was brought down from High Force by slushing it down wooden flumes to the mill, using water as a lubricant. An inclined tramway two miles in length was built to Braithwaite. However, due to unstable prices, the mine once again became unprofitable and the banks foreclosed in 1879. Around 5,300 tons of barytes had been produced.

The mine was not reopened until about 1907, and this time zinc was the main product. Fifty men were employed, and a new mill was constructed, but in 1911 the mine closed again due to bankruptcy. A new company opened the following year and carried out modifications to the mill, installing an Elmore flotation plant to separate the ore, one of the first to be used in Britain. They also spent a lot of money driving a new level, Zero Level, but the returns could not support this heavy investment and yet again the mine closed. When the Great War created new demands and a subsidy was payable on zinc the mine was reopened, and the mill brought up to date with the latest technology. After the war the subsidy was removed, and it closed

again in 1922. This pattern of intermittent working was to continue over the years due to the varied demand for minerals, and to the uncertainties of mining.

During the 1930s barytes was mined from High Force, which had not been worked since 1880. A track was driven up the fellside so that equipment and ore could be transported by lorry, and on the outbreak of the Second World War the mine was acquired by Tampimex Oil Products Ltd, who widened the track and built a new mill to produce barytes, which was used in the manufacture of explosives. It is this mill which can be seen at the present time. The track proved unsatisfactory and an aerial ropeway was constructed from High Force to the mill, 740 ft below, traces of which still exist. During the winter of 1947 the mine was totally cut off by snow for six weeks, and when access was regained it was found to be completely flooded. As pumping equipment was not available it was decided to close the mine, having raised some 35,000 tons of barytes. Two years later the La Porte Chemical Co took over and, having established that there were reserves of 100,000 tons of barytes, decided to drive an incline to a height of 325 ft above No 3 Level, and then to put up a rise to drain the flooded High Force workings from below. The incline was driven for 1,100 ft without finding the vein, and a forty foot rise had been put in a short distance from the top when the Company had a change of policy and pulled out.

The mine was disused for eight years until, in 1960, McKechnie Brothers of Widnes restarted the operation and soon broke through into the workings above, which had been flooded since 1947. They too mined barytes, much of which was taken down the La Porte Incline using heavy scrapers dragged by winches and assisted by water. Some of this machinery is still in place. The Company carried out an evaluation of reserves in No 1 Level, and estimated 40,000 tons at 10% zinc, but this was not developed and McKechnies closed the mine in 1966 when the known barytes reserves in the High Force area were mined out.

Over the next fifteen years three more companies attempted to work the lower part of the mine for lead and zinc, but none was successful. What may well prove to be the final attempt commenced in 1984, when the New Coledale Mining Co was formed to extract zinc, lead and barytes from the low levels on a part-time basis. The first task was to get the mill into working order and to restore the entrances to No 1 and Zero Levels. At first the Company concentrated on barytes, but later shifted to zinc. This operation ended in 1990 when a massive collapse occurred in Zero Level, long known as the 'Unsuccessful Level'. Water backed up to No 1 Level, so it was necessary to rescue equipment ahead of the rising water. The scale of the collapse was such that to clear it was beyond the resources of the Company and all work was stopped. The mine was on a short lease, and the land owners, the National Trust, are not in favour of a working mine in the Lake District fells, so it seems unlikely that mining will ever again take place at Force Crag. As a consequence of the more or less continuous history of mining, from the mid 19th century to the present time, the mine is much better preserved than most, and so it is unique. It is to be hoped that it will not be destroyed and landscaped like the mines of Greenside and Carrock, but will be preserved as part of our heritage.

Alston and the North Pennines

The area with which we will now concern ourselves is the highest and most northerly part of the Pennine Chain situated in the county of Cumbria, an area which is, without doubt, one of the most inhospitable in the whole of England. Yet it is an area which has hidden some of England's greatest mineral wealth, a wealth which is being exploited in some small way to this day.

The mining of lead and its associated ores is an ancient industry which can trace its roots back to Roman times and possibly beyond. The Romans operated lead mines throughout their huge empire, especially in Spain, so it would seem certain that they would know of the North Pennine's wealth and exploit it, given that they were so close to the nearby great wall of Hadrian.

After the Romans little is known of the fate of this area although the use of Anglo / Danish terminology in local mining dialect suggests that the mineral wealth of the area was appreciated.

After the Norman Conquest, evidence of mining activity is non-existent until we have the first recorded note in 1130 for rent of a silver mine on Alston Moor (silver was often extracted from lead ore) which was a hundred shillings, an astronomical sum. From that time there are sporadic reports of other silver mines in the area, perhaps supplying the mint known to be operating in Carlisle. It was around this time that whole new markets for lead ore were opening up with a massive increase in the construction of religious houses and castles for the new aristocracy. Indeed, lead was not only roofing English buildings; it is known that one hundred cartloads were despatched to Clairvaux in France. One can do little but wonder at a journey which would have taken lead from the rugged moorland of Alston by packhorse to the Tyne. From there it would have been shipped to Rotterdam before going on to Clairvaux.

In the 13th century the mines changed hands several times under the ownership of the kings of Scotland, but little is known of mining in the 14th century. The 15th century saw a considerable growth of activity and, by 1468, the English king Edward IV had made agreements enabling him to receive a twelfth part of all the precious metals found. Throughout the rest of the century the kings of England had active interests in the area, especially in the mine of Fletcheras, between the South Tyne and the Nent Valleys where there is still evidence of ancient workings.

These primitive workings continued under royal patronage until the 16th century when Henry VIII appointed a German, Joachim Hoegstre, to be his master of mines. Hoegstre was the father of Daniel Höchstetter who appears later in the development of the copper industry at Keswick and Coniston. From Hoegstre's work sprang a far more professional approach to the development of metal mining in England and more particularly on Alston Moor. Despite a slight setback with the dissolution of the monasteries the lead industry continued to flourish and by the end of the 17th century it stood ready for the great leap forward in technological advancement that was the industrial revolution.

The mineral rights owners for most of the Alston Moor area at the beginning of the 18th century were the Earls of Derwentwater. But following their disastrous involvement in the rebellion of 1715 the estates and mineral rights passed

to the Crown, and in 1735 were granted to The Royal Hospital for Seamen at Greenwich, better known as the Greenwich Hospital. It was under their tutelage that the area became one of the chief centres for technological advancement of the lead industry for the next two centuries.

The other factor of crucial importance for the area was the granting in 1692 of a charter to "The Governor and Company for Smelting Down Lead with Pittcoale and Seacole". This later became known as the London Lead Company and, after 1704, the Quaker Lead Company, becoming the largest single employer of men on Alston Moor until the end of the 19th century. The Company operated from two bases, Nenthead and Garrigill, but it should be remembered that it also had interests in other areas of England and Wales. It is important to note that the Company's original charter makes no mention of getting ore but is only concerned with smelting. However, it was a small step from smelting to placing the Company in a position from where it could also control the supply to keep the mills working.

Before the London Lead Company began to work systematically the Alston Moor area, most of the mining had been carried out in an extremely piecemeal way by small companies or individuals who could not afford to develop the mines to their full potential. However, by 1780 the mines under the control of the Company were completely modernised, and were brought together under a single system of development and working.

The London Lead Company leased the mines from the Greenwich Hospital for a duty of one-fifth or one-sixth of the ore actually produced. Initially they then sold the ore back to the mining companies for smelting, but by 1767 the commissioners of the Hospital decided to smelt their own and built a mill at Langley, where they were close to coal supplies. The fall in the price of lead in the 19th century led to reductions in duty paid to as low as one-ninth.

The Greenwich Hospital commissioners appointed two receivers in the area to oversee the mining and smelting activities and to ensure that the Hospital's mines were being worked efficiently. Perhaps the two most famous receivers worked in the 1770s and were responsible for one of the greatest engineering projects in the area. In 1775 Richard Walton and John Smeaton reported to the Hospital commissioners that a drainage level should be driven from Alston to Nenthead with the purpose of draining existing mines and also exploring and hopefully locating new mineral veins at depth. The route eventually chosen followed the course of the River Nent and the tunnel driving commenced in July 1776, the tunnel eventually being nine feet square and nearly five miles long. The Nent Force Level, as it was known, was built so large in order to act as a canal with which to bring out the spoil (waste rock) created by the tunnelling. The canal went as far as Nentsberry Haggs Shaft, some three miles from its entrance, where a massive 'step' of about 160 ft was created before the level continued in normal proportions to its end at the Brewery Shaft in Nenthead. The level became something of a tourist attraction and Sopwith (1833) described a journey along it.

It is navigated by boats 30 ft in length which are propelled in four feet water by means of sticks projecting from the sides of the level; and thus may be enjoyed the singular novelty of sailing a few miles underground, and beholding with perfect safety the various rocks that it passes through....The hanging rocks suspended over the entrance with the Romantic scenery adjoining and the neighbouring waterfall renders a visit, even to the exterior, highly interesting; but this is much increased by a subterranean excursion....The old and sometime grotesque dresses worn on such occasion add to the mirth and cheerfulness which prevail – while the fine effect of vocal or instrumental music and the exercise of propelling the boat add to the singular feeling which is excited by so bold an adventure.

Regrettably for so magnificent a venture, the Nent Force level discovered only one new vein to justify the £80,000 that it cost and the sixty-six years it took to complete.

The London Lead Company continued its involvement with Alston Moor and was in the forefront of many of the changes affecting the mining and metallurgical industry all through the 18th and 19th centuries. Indeed, many new inventions sprang from the area such as Pattinson's smelting techniques, Attwood's slime trunking machine and Brunton's continuous cloth separator. The London Lead Company was without doubt one of the most successful companies to have operated anywhere in Britain, but in 1882 it put its Alston Moor operation up for sale. Unlike most companies it did this while still making consistent profits, but the continuing slide in the price of lead throughout the latter half of the 19th century meant that profits were decreasing.

The debt which the area owes to the London Lead Company, is considerable, for not only was it involved in mining and smelting but also in every other aspect of life in the North Pennines. It sponsored schools, brass bands, chapels, sporting events and welfare services. But why this apparent altruism? Hunt (1970) explains it thus:

Efficient management meant controlling the labour force at home as well as at work and educating the next generation into a proper sense of discipline.

The way in which companies paid their miners in the North Pennines deserves an explanation as they did not just earn a basic wage. The bargain system operated in the area, described by Forster (1821) as:

The miners take a piece of ground, commonly called a length, in which they propose to raise ore....according to the richness of the mine or working. A length of ground is commonly either twelve, fifteen or twenty fathoms, and the price of procuring the Ore depends much upon the hardness, the expense of drawing the Stone or Ore out of the Mine, and the probable quantity of metal that can be raised.

The bargain system did not just end with the getting of the ore; Sopwith (1833) writes:

The bargain usually includes not only the labour in the mine but also for gunpowder and candles, for the conveyance of the stone or ore, etc. to the day or outside of the mine, and also for the washing and preparing it as to be fit for smelting. It is by the bing of 8 cwt of ore, that the price of working is fixed.

This system meant that the mine owners were getting quite a good deal – payment by results. This system could be extended to almost any underground occupation so that shaft sinking and level driving could all be 'bargained' per yard. The only occupations paid a weekly wage were surface workers such as blacksmiths and smelter operatives. Naturally, setting the bargains needed a high degree of skill on both sides. The mine owners' agent had to know the mine well in order not to set the pay too high, while the miners had to have an excellent knowledge of both general mining and the particular place concerned so as not to set their price too low. Sopwith (1833) makes the point:

It may easily be perceived how much it is in the interest of the working miner to be well acquainted with the various appearances in strata and veins, that he may judge of and make his bargains accordingly. Hence a spirit of enquiry is created, which naturally extends to other subjects and the miners generally possess a degree of shrewdness and intelligence rarely found in a labouring class of people.

The bargain system continued to the end of the London Lead Company's reign in 1882, although it had changed greatly and the miners had become virtual wage earners.

The London Lead Company sold its entire holding in mines and mills to the Tynedale and Nent Head Zinc Company for £30,562 7s 6d. (Raistrick, 1977) and moved the centre of operations to Middleton in Teesdale. Regrettably, during this time the new company did little new development and this, coupled with a plunge in the price of lead and zinc, forced the company to sell its assets in 1896.

The buyer was a Belgian company, The Vieille Montagne Zinc Company, with substantial interests elsewhere in Britain, especially in Wales. It continued development around Nenthead and was responsible for many technical innovations, not least the incredible use of air and water at the Brewery Shaft near the smelt mill. In 1910, following a fire which destroyed the old mill, a new mill was built (the remains of which are still there, in use as a bus garage), at the time the most up-to-date mill in the country. This was followed by development work in the Nentsberry Haggs Level including the sinking of the 415ft deep Wellhope Shaft which was working from 1923 to 1938 and produced over 250,000 tons of rough ore (Raistrick & Jennings, 1965). The Company also developed the Rotherhope Fell Mine and these ventures, along with some reworking of spoil, enabled the Company to keep in operation until 1949.

The leases were then taken up by Anglo Austral Mines Ltd, who began to rework the spoil for fluorspar as well as developing the mines at Nentsberry for zinc production – though little was ever processed. This Company had relinquished the lease by December 1961 and following this, despite the lease being taken on several occasions, the area has remained idle.

This idleness has been to the advantage of some, namely the modern mine explorer. The mines around Alston Moor offer a richness of industrial archaeology rarely equalled in any other part of Britain.

The underground workings are characterised by two peculiarities which set them apart from other areas in Cumbria. The first is the way in which the tunnels and levels are often stone arched, and this has contributed to the way in which the underground environment has survived so well. This stone arching is all the more remarkable in that the stone was often quarried outside and trammed into the mine. Secondly, the ore often occurs not in the more familiar veins but in massive 'flats', described in 1833 by Sopwith:

The ore in these flats (as the name implies) lies horizontally, and the excavations in them are several yards in breadth... Flats occasionally reach to great extent like a regular stratum, and terminate suddenly by a back or joint in the strata, and not in a wedge-like shape.

It is hard to predict the future of the Alston Moor area for it is virtually certain that mineral veins remain which may yield enough ore to make their exploitation commercially viable. Time alone will tell.

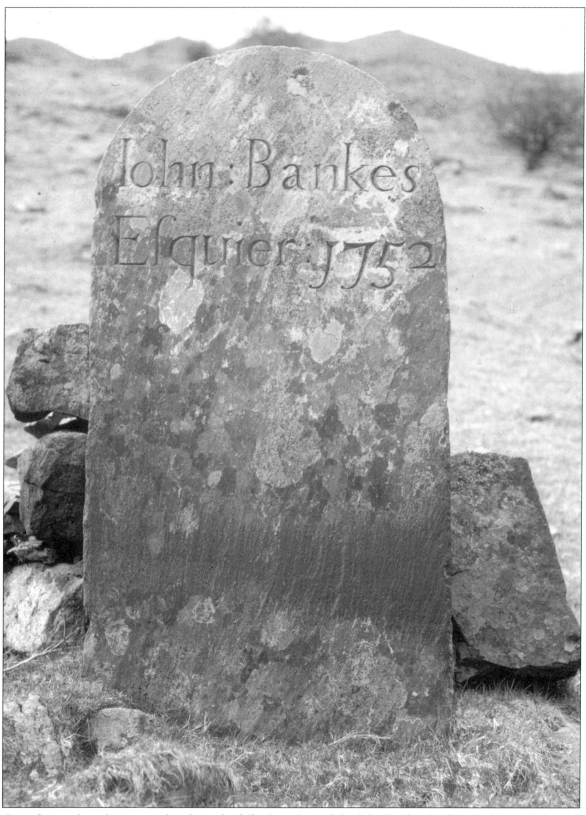

One of several marker stones that determined the boundary of the John Bankes land at the Borrowdale Wad Mine. Unfortunately vandals have been at work in recent times and one stone has had to be remade.

Photo: *Peter Fleming*

The walls of the guardhouse outside the portal of Gilbert's Stage at the Borrowdale Wad Mine stand like a sentinel after a century of abandonment: many the poor miner who passed through the doorway under the watchful eye of the management: many the wad picker's lantern that flickered at night as the wind blew over the dark spoil heaps.

Driven by muscle, sweat and probably blood and a few tears, the coffin level of the Old Men's Stage at the Borrowdale Wad Mine meanders into the fell towards the Grand Pipe. As well as hammers and wedges, the old men used fire as a means of cracking the rock. Brushwood was heaped against the face and burned until the rock became hot. Then water (and some say vinegar) was applied, causing the rock to splinter.

Photo: *Dave Bridge*

In the Borrowdale Wad Mine the deposit of wad known as the Grand Pipe is thought to have been discovered during the reign of Queen Elizabeth I and was worked to a great depth – well over 300ft – over a period of some 250 years. A safe descent of the upper part of the Grand Pipe can be made from its intersection with Farey's Stage.

Photo: *David Bridge*

This view, of the oldest high workings at Greenside, shows the large craters high on the flank of Stybarrow Dodd. These are the results of mining subsidence within the stopes of High Horse Level. Below are the upper dressing floors and fan tips from the High Horse Level.

Photo: *Mike Mitchell*

High Horse Level some 1600ft (500m) above sea level under the flanks of Stybarrow Dodd was the main working level of Greenside Mine in the early part of the 19th century. The extent of these upper workings can be judged by the quantity of spoil trammed out. During the 1830s the Greenside Mining Company built a lead smelter further down the valley with a mile long flue. The line of the collapsed flue can be seen running up the crest of Stang beyond.

Photo: *Dave Bridge*

Within the depths of the Greenside Lead Mine miners constructed a ladder-way running from the main Lucy Tongue Level up to the ancient workings of Glencoynedale Level. The purpose of the ladder-way was to provide a means of escape from the mine in case of an emergency. The ladder-way follows a series of vertical shafts in which were also large cast iron water pipes carrying water down to power equipment in the machine rooms on the Lucy Tongue Level.

Photo: *Mike Mitchell*

Two photographs showing the machine rooms on the Lucy Tongue Level of the Greenside Lead Mine. These now empty rooms once housed the compressors and generators which were the instruments of success for this large Lakeland lead mine before power was provided by the National Grid.

Photos: *Mike Mitchell*

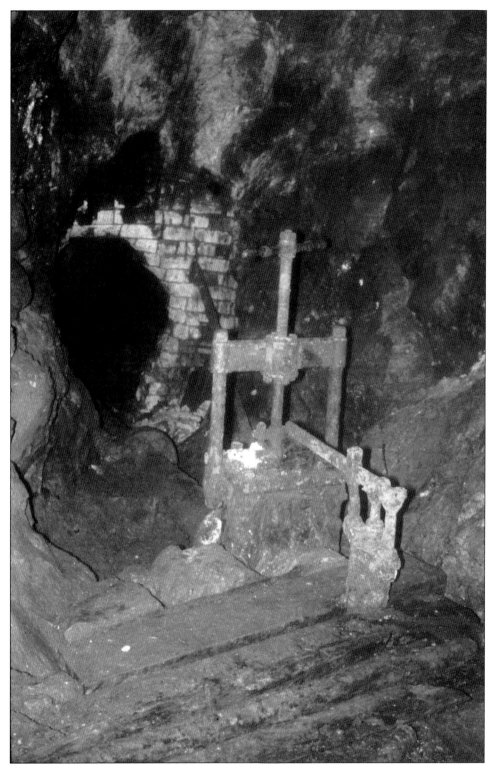

The Willie Shaft, sunk from the Low Horse Level during the 1850s, drew the water for its hydraulic engines from flooded workings behind the dams of the High Horse and Glencoyne levels. The penstock valve in the picture is sited behind the main High Horse Level dam at the head of a rise, down which the pipes plummet. The dams were breached during the 1930s, long after the hydraulic engines became redundant, to provide a means of escape via the Glencoyne Level in the event of an accident.

Photo: *Ian Matheson*

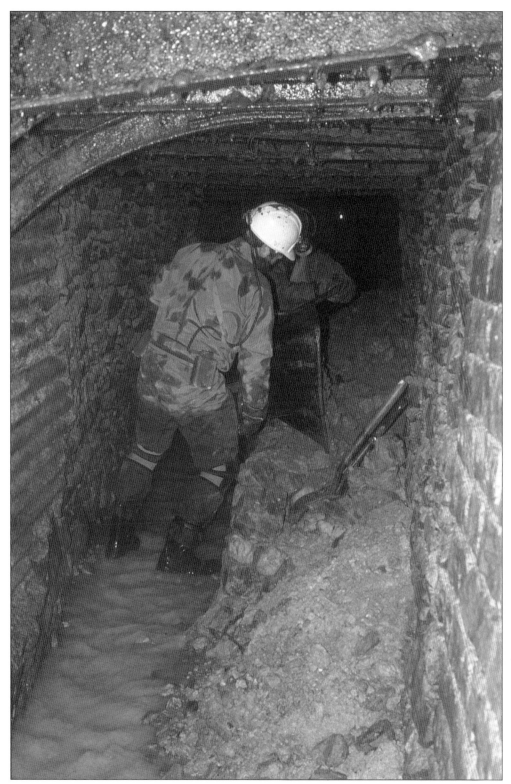

For many years the only way into the Lucy Tongue Level at Greenside was via the Glencoynedale Adit, and a 700 ft descent down the old ladder-way. In 1994 mine explorers obtained permission to re-open the Lucy Tongue Level portal and clear the level. Three years later, after considerable expense and hard labour, they managed to clear a way through. The photograph shows a team tipping waste material cleared from the dig up ahead.

Photo: *Ian Matheson*

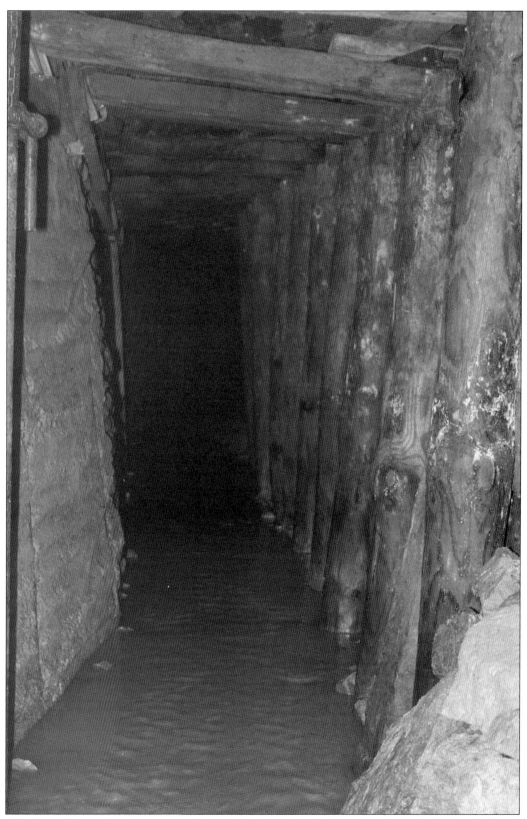

Part of the Lucy Tongue Level was considered extremely unstable and new timbering had to be installed to support the roof.

Photo: *Ian Matheson*

The twin tunnels in High Horse Level at Greenside were once part of an underground water storage system. The level was bricked up to create a reservoir to feed the hydraulic engine on the Lucy Tongue Level far below. When the mine was connected to the National Grid the reservoirs became disused and were broken open.

Photo: *Ian Matheson*

A shot firing chest remains as an artefact within the High Horse Level at Greenside.

Photo: *Ken Geddes*

To ensure a constant supply of water to the ore dressing site and later the power house at Greenside mine the level of Kepple Cove Tarn was raised with a 40ft high earth dam. On 29th October 1927 a cloudburst washed away part of the embankment and a great flood swept down the valley damaging houses and shops near Glenridding bridge. The old dam was replaced by one of concrete (shown here) which itself burst in 1931 and was never repaired. This gate valve, still in situ, had been salvaged from the old dam.

Photo: *David Bridge*

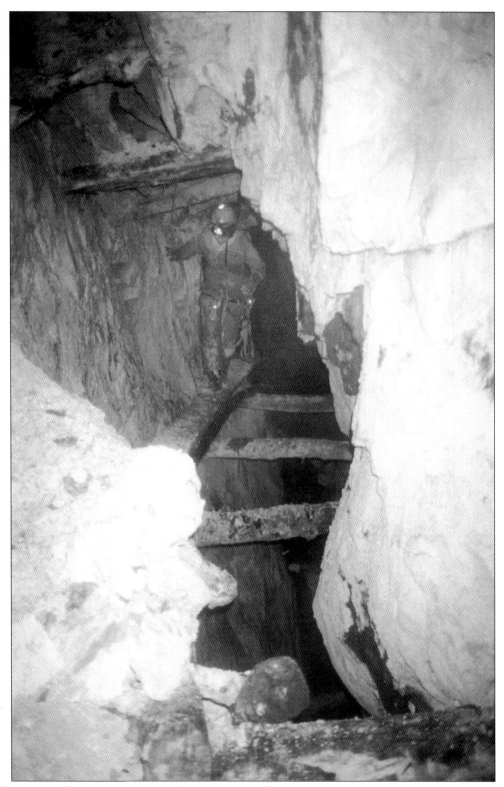

The Tilberthwaite North Lode was a productive copper vein and the underground workings on the lode can still be reached from the Waterfall Level at the head of Tilberthwaite Gill.

The workings connect with a rise from Horse Crag Deep Adit 500ft below. Today the remaining floor timbers are rotten and require great care.

Photo: *David Bridge*

This photograph shows a working party within the Paddy End workings of the Coniston Mine. The group are inspecting some of the extremely dangerous sections of the mine in the Puddingstone Level.

Photo: *Mike Mitchell*

Since mining for wolfram began Carrock Mine has seen highly productive periods when the tungsten demand, especially for the manufacture of armaments, was high, but there have also been periods of closure and the mine has now been abandoned. Here we see part of the plant left over from recent operations on the Harding Vein.

The strong N-S quartz veins to the east of Carrock Fell were considered barren by the early miners in their search for lead and copper. It was not until the turn of the 20th century that their true value was recognised and wolfram began to be extracted for the strategic metal tungsten for which Carrock Mine has since become famous.

Photos: *Ronnie Calvin*

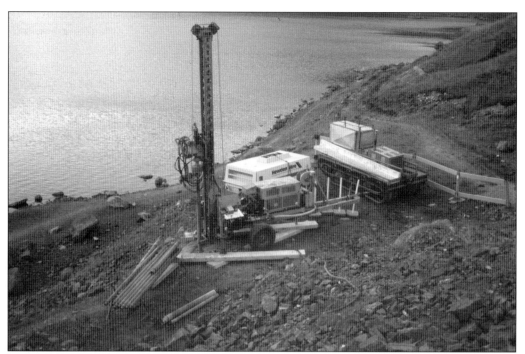

On the shore of Levers Water, Coniston, a drilling rig has been set up to locate Woodends Level below. Eventually the drilling equipment broke into the level which was then sealed with concrete.

The team of three who constructed a 'catwalk' across a stope in the Coniston Mine clean themselves up after their work. The catwalk, which was constructed on 1st February 1987, allowed explorers easier access into the inner reaches of the extensive Top Level in the mine. The construction became known as 'MAGS Catwalk', after the initials of the construction team.

Photos: *Mike Mitchell*

'The best dressed of underground explorers'. The wear and tear of industrial archaeology in a Lakeland ore mine.
Photo: *Mike Mitchell*

The signalling hammer at the head of the ladderway from the Lucy Tongue Level to the Alma illustrates that even in the depths of a Lakeland lead mine technological advancement recognises no bounds. Equipment, tools and probably dynamite were hauled up the rise by a compressed-air winch bolted to the staging at the side of the manhole. The signalling hammer was controlled by a wire running down the rise to the main level below.

Photo: *Ian Matheson*

Dynamite became available during the 1870s and has been used in a multitude of forms and for a multitude of purposes ever since. The early varieties were based on a mixture of nitro-glycerine and kieselguhr, a diatomaceous earth. Other variants were nitro-glycerine and sand (which became unstable in water), and nitro-glycerine and gun cotton, which was probably the case in the picture above. The term 'powder' is still used in today's coal industry and covers a range of explosive materials, much the same as the word 'dynamite' is still used in the slate quarries when referring to blasting gelatines. The metal boxes beneath the dynamite packages contained No. 6 detonators. The picture was taken in Carr's Mine, Nenthead.
Photo: *Mike Mitchell*

Deeper and deeper into the depths of Greenside. In the lower section of the rise between the High and Low levels, the wooden ladders give way to cumbersome chain ladders which swing alarmingly in the confines of the narrow shaft.

Photo: *Ian Matheson*

The Alma Level, worked between 1937 and 1961, was the main haulage road in the Alma ore-shoot. Driven along the vein, two hundred feet above the Lucy Tongue Level, ore from the stopes above was loaded into tubs, run to the end of the tunnel, then tipped into a second stope to fall clattering to the hoppers on the Lucy Tongue. The black strands hanging from the timber in the roof of the level are the stems of a rare fungus. Until quite recently the fungus formed a heavy curtain across the level, making passage uncomfortable and more than a little eerie.

Photo: *Ian Matheson*

A hopper stands in a sub-level of the Alma ore-shoot. Tubs were run under the hoppers then filled with veinstone blasted from the stope above. Note the kibble standing between the tramlines. This is made from a length of rubber conveyer belt, strapped together with iron bands. It was used for winching tools and explosives from the Lucy Tongue Level to the workings of the Alma.

Photo: *Ian Matheson*

Iron ladder and compressed-air pipes ascending a rise in the Alma workings, Greenside Mine.

Photo: *Ian Matheson*

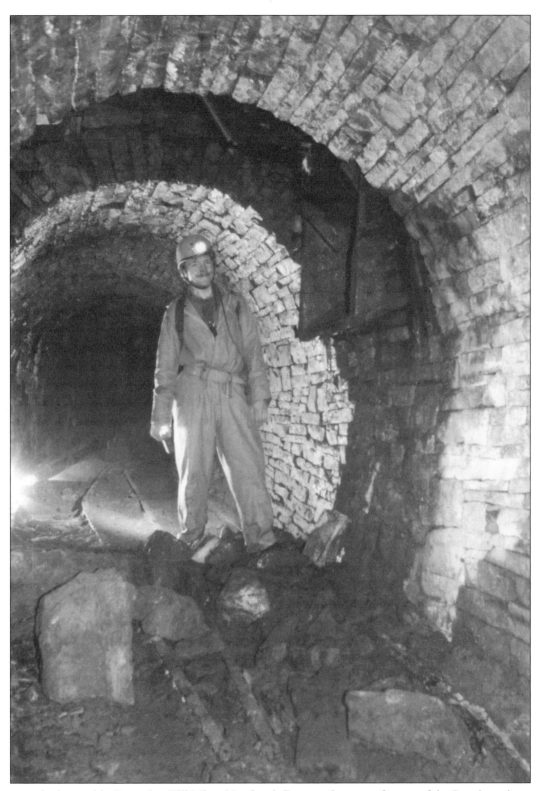

A stone-arched tunnel in Brownley Hill Mine, Nenthead. Stone arches are a feature of the Pennine mines – one thing that makes them remarkable is that, in most instances, the stone was quarried outside and brought in specifically for the purpose. Note the double sets of tramlines. The set on the right was a siding for tubs being loaded from the ore hopper, while the set on the left was a loop for through traffic.

Photo: *Sheila and Anton Thomas*

Mining still goes on in the Lakeland mountains, albeit on a small scale. These photographs are taken in the Horse Crag slate mine, Coniston. The proprietor, George Tarr, collects a clog of slate and with the help of an assistant lifts it by block and tackle onto a truck for transporting out of the mine.

Horse Crag mine was developed in an old copper mine level, and has considerable historic significance for the area. It became the location for Slater Bob's mine in Arthur Ransome's *Pigeon Post*. It was also worked for many years during the 20th century by the well-known Shaw family of Coniston.

Photos: *Alastair Cameron*

LAKELAND'S MINING HERITAGE – WOLFRAM

by David Blundell

Wolfram mining in Cumbria was confined to one site, Carrock Mine, situated in Grainsgill – a tributary of the River Caldew – four and a half miles south of Caldbeck and twelve miles west of Penrith. Carrock was the only locality outside the counties of Cornwall and Devon to have produced wolfram. Along with Castle-an Dinas Mine, near St Austell in Cornwall (worked 1915 to 1958), it was the only mine in the country where wolfram was the sole ore produced.

The mine has worked spasmodically since 1854, but never for very long as mining is only viable when the price of tungsten is at its peak. The last period of working finished in October 1981.

Wolfram was previously produced in Britain as a by-product of the tin mines of Devon and Cornwall and was, prior to 1898, regarded by miners as a nuisance in ore dressing, due to the difficulties of separating it from the cassiterite (tin ore). After this date, demand rose for wolfram for use in the production of tungsten high speed steel and tungsten cutting tools. In Cornwall the mines of Camborne–Redruth area dominated the production of wolfram, with the mines of East Pool and Agar, South Crofty, Carn Brea and Tincroft being the major producers. Carrock Mine, even in its heyday was never a major producer of wolfram. For example, in 1916 Carrock produced twenty tons of WO_3 concentrate, slightly under 5.5% of the total national production for that year. With the closure of most of the Cornish mines, British production of tungsten ores in world terms is now insignificant. Wolfram is now imported from the USA, Australia, Canada, Bolivia, Portugal and the Republic of Korea.

The ores produced at Carrock Mine were galena (PbS), wolfram ($Fe_1Mn_1WO_3$) and scheelite ($CaWO_4$), the last two named being the chief ores of tungsten. Traditionally this metal was almost exclusively used for making the filaments in light bulbs, vacuum and x-ray tubes. With the growing use of nuclear reactors for generating electricity, tungsten has become important as a cladding for fuel rods containing uranium and plutonium oxides because it is non-reactive, has a high melting point and is a good conductor of heat. It is widely used in cemented carbides, tool steels and tungsten metal mill products.

The geology of the Carrock area consists of several mineralised veins dipping west at about 80° and tending northwards across the lower part of Grainsgill Beck, where they have been worked from Carrock Mine. The veins traverse the northernmost outcrop of the Skiddaw granite (which is mostly converted to gneiss) and the adjacent hornfels and gabbro rocks of the north. The upper parts of the granite in the gneissenised zones are above Grainsgill and take the form of a dome which attains its maximum elevation between the eastern spur of Coombe Height, and the Caldew and Grainsgill valleys. The roof contact falls fairly steeply in all directions to pass beneath the metamorphosed Skiddaw slates. The three principal veins, going from west to east are the Smith Vein, the Harding Vein and the Emerson Vein.

The mine is situated in the steep sided valley of the Grainsgill Beck, with the main adit at a height of 1,115 ft. The veins cross the beck at approximately 90°, rendering the mine easily worked by a series of adit levels driven north and south into the valley sides. No workings have been developed below the main adit, and as the adit is above the valley bottom it was not necessary to resort to pumping or winding to work the mine. Ore from upper workings was scraped and tipped down a series of internal ore-passes into hoppers on the main adit level and then run into tubs and hauled out of the mine to the mill. The country rock is competent and the majority of the stopes and levels are self-supporting. Only small quantities of timber were required, where the levels pass through the overlying boulder clay.

Up to 1913 all rock drilling was done by hand but following the take-over of the mine by the Carrock Mining Syndicate, an air-compressor, driven by a gas engine, was installed to power three rock drills. In the last phase of working a number of Joy Sullivan double drum compressed air winches were in use in the mine to scrape ore along higher sub-levels to ore-passes, replacing the method previously used of hand-loading wheelbarrows and tipping the ore down the passes. In development drives in the mine, Eimco compressed air loading shovels were used to load rock and ore into mine tubs. The method of operation is to run the loader forward on its rails into a pile of rock left after blasting, with the shovel lowered. With a mine tub coupled to the rear of the loader, the bucket on the loading shovel swings rapidly from the horizontal to the vertical throwing the material back into the tub. This minimises the amount of back breaking labour involved in loading rock and ore into tubs.

The principal workings have been on the Harding Vein which varies in width from a few inches in the granite to over five feet in the gabbro. It consists mainly of quartz with distributions of wolfram and scheelite, together with a range of other minerals. This vein has been proved to a length of over 1,500 ft, on both sides of the Grainsgill valley, by surface and underground work.

A little exploration was carried out on the Smith Vein in the early part of the century from the surface where it was found to contain arsenopyrite and scheelite. Later, the 1942-43 exploration cross cut to the Harding Vein was extended westwards to the Smith Vein. It was explored to the north and south with not very satisfactory results but was subsequently worked during the latest phase of operations, giving a vein width of approximately two feet. The Smith Vein has not been worked to the south of Grainsgill Beck.

The Emerson Vein has a long history of spasmodic working on five levels on the northern slope of the valley and one trial level on the Coombe Height (south) side. All the adits have now caved in and the levels are for the most part inaccessible. The wolfram content of this vein is said to have been rich in places, but had a very patchy distribution. In early 1980, a cross cut was driven east from the adit level of the mine to the Emerson Vein, and some driving was completed to the north for about 700 ft, but with very little production. This part of the mine has poor natural ventilation.

The earliest recorded working in the area took place in 1852, by F W Emerson of Penzance, Cornwall, who was intending to mine for copper or lead ores on the east-west veins which are about 200 yards long and run between the Harding and Emerson veins half way up Brandy Gill. A mining lease for lead was not granted by the owner of the mineral rights and so Emerson turned his attention to the most easterly of the veins, which now bears his name. Work was also carried out on a small trial in Brandy Gill. All work had ceased by 1858.

In 1863, Leicester M Hutchinson & Co, and later from 1875-77, M Hutchinson & Co, worked the lead veins in Brandy Gill. Two levels were driven in the west bank of the gill and joined by a rise. It is reported that there was a promising show of galena at first but it was later found that the ore-body was very small. Production in 1872 was four tons of galena, giving three tons of lead, and in 1874, five and a half tons of galena giving four tons of lead and 29 ounces of silver. In 1872-73, small scale workings took place on the Harding Vein on the south side of Grainsgill Valley, at the outcrop of the vein. Wolfram was produced by hand-sorting but no production records exist.

In 1902, Carrock Mines Ltd, under James Harding of Penrith, took a take-note for the mine and commenced prospecting works, mainly on the vein subsequently named after him and also at three levels on the Emerson Vein. By 1905 the mine had closed having produced thirty-seven tons of wolfram ore.

The mine did not stand idle for long, for in 1906 two Germans, William Boss and Frederick Boehm, re-financed the operations, and under the name of the Cumbrian Mining Co Ltd the mill was extended and for a time both day and night shifts operated at the mine and the mill. The work force reached a peak of one hundred and five, evenly split between the surface and underground workers. Production averaged twenty three tons per annum, valued at £60 per ton for most of the period, but reaching £118 per ton in 1907, when

sixty four tons were produced. Four tons of arsenic were produced in 1911, valued at £5 per ton. By the end of 1911 production had ceased and the following year the Company was in liquidation with only the caretaker, William Wilson of Caldbeck, remaining on the payroll.

1913 saw the formation of the Carrock Mining Syndicate, a group of steel manufacturers under the management of Captain Anthony Wilson, of Thornthwaite Grange, near Keswick, who also managed the Thornthwaite and Threlkeld mines. The work was partly government-financed, the mill being reconstructed and equipped with hand-picking belts, crushing rolls, gigs, screens, Deister sand tables, Wilfey tables and Vanners. The concentrates were roasted in a half-ton capacity hand-raked furnace, to remove the arsenic, which was collected from the flues. Power was supplied by generators driven by pelton wheels, assisted during times of water shortage by a gas engine. The remains of this operation can still be seen by the side of the beck adjacent to the Harding Vein (south). Stoping was carried out in the Penny Level (Harding Vein south), then Harding Level on the vein (north), along with some work on the Emerson Vein. Almost 14,000 tons of ore were mined, and 10,116 tons milled, which produced almost 100 tons of 16% WO_3 concentrate.

With the end of the First World War, government support was withdrawn, while at the same time the market was swamped with stocks of tungsten concentrates as governments off-loaded their strategic stock piles. This caused the complete collapse of the market for tungsten concentrates and they became virtually impossible to sell. The previous year the same concentrate would have fetched £178 per ton. By late 1918 the work force had dropped from around 100 to 25 at the time of closure of the underground workings. In 1919 a few workers were involved in washing zinc blende prior to the mill being dismantled later that year.

The site remained silent until the fall of Burma in 1942. Burma was at that time an important source of tungsten. Faced with a possible shortage, the country again turned to Carrock. The Ministry of Supply, in conjunction with Non-Ferrous Minerals Development Ltd, attempted to prove the existence of 80,000 to 100,000 tons of tungsten ore. The exploratory work commenced in June 1942 and continued until October 1943. The services of a Canadian Royal Engineers tunnelling company was used, as no local skilled labour was available. The thirty five Canadians were billeted in barracks built at the mine. At the end of 1942, twenty five Canadians left for other duties and their place was taken by Spanish Pioneers and Italian POWs. A new crosscut level was driven to the Harding Vein (No 2 or Canadian Level, the present entrance to the mine), some sixty feet below the old Harding (No 1) Level. The crosscut was extended to the Smith Vein, as well as driving north and south on the Harding Vein, totalling two thousand feet at a cost of £5 per foot, with a further £5,000 spent on compressors, pipelines, buildings and roads. It was proposed to erect a small mill (suitable for incorporation into a larger set-up later) but this was never built. Sampling was carried out on the Harding Vein (north and south), Smith and Emerson Veins, proving the existence of 51,000 tons of wolfram in excess of 1.09% mineral. No stoping was carried out and the Ministry of Supply closed the project down in October 1943, having declined to carry out a programme of diamond drilling,

recommended by their consultants, Messrs James Jackson and J D Wilson, who claimed that the target had been reached. By this time the tungsten supply position had improved.

The next period of interest in the mine was in 1951-52 with the outbreak of the Korean War (Korea being an important producer of wolfram) and a rise in the price of tungsten metal. Durham Chemicals took an interest in the mine, but encountered stiff opposition for any development from the National Trust and various local bodies, due to the mine's situation in the then proposed Lake District National Park. Before the problem could be resolved the price of tungsten fell again and Durham Chemicals withdrew without carrying out any work on site.

In 1971 World Wide Energy (UK) Ltd, a wholly-owned subsidiary of WECO Development Corporation of Denver, Colorado, USA, leased the mine and 3,500 acres surrounding it. Their assessment of the ore deposits was based wholly on the results of the exploration of 1942-43, with only a limited sampling taking place for confirmation. A mill was constructed and some underground development took place on the old Harding Level. The mill ran for only a few weeks in 1972, on 230 tons of wolfram ore with a grade of 1.55%, before the company decided to withdraw. They put the mill on standby in July 1972, after spending £250,000. The price of Wolfram had fallen from £38 per ton in 1970 to only £16 in 1972.

The shutdown lasted until 1976 when WECO granted a one year lease to Carrock Fell Mining Ltd (a subsidiary of Amalgamated Industrials Ltd) with an option to enter into a joint venture agreement at the end of the lease period in August 1977. Robertson Research

International Ltd, of North Wales, was appointed as technical consultant in September 1976. The mine and mill came into production in April 1977, with the aim of processing 12,500 tonnes per annum, or 60 tonnes per eight hour day. The operation became profitable during the first six months of 1978 and employed sixteen men underground, with a further eight in the mill. At the end of the option period the joint venture was taken up. Twelve months later Carrock Fell Mining was purchased by the National Carbonising Co (Energy) Ltd, who continued the joint venture on the same basis as the previous company – 62.14% shares, with World Wide Energy (UK) Ltd at 37.86%. Production of ore was running at 16,000 tonnes per annum, giving 200 tonnes of 65% wolfram concentrates. Ore was produced from the Harding Vein (north and south), Wilson Vein, Waterfall Vein and from the Emerson Vein via a cross cut driven from the Canadian Level in 1979-80.

The workforce totalled thirty when the mine closed in October 1981. The price of wolfram concentrates had again fallen, coupled with the company's difficulty in disposing of the fine tailings from the mill, due to the restrictive regulations on the size of the lagoons imposed by the National Park Authority. They had to resort to pumping them as a slurry into the old stopes on the Harding Vein (south). Problems were encountered regarding the high levels of arsenic found in the coarse tailings from the mill, which made them unsuitable for use as an aggregate, because of the risk of poisonous dust being released into the atmosphere.

The mine was put into mothballs on a care and maintenance basis. A new company purchased the lease in November 1982, part of the Minworth group of companies, based in Derbyshire. No further work was carried out and in the spring of 1986 mining and milling equipment was removed from site, trackwork lifted, and smaller buildings removed.

It is notable that in the past the threat, or actuality, of war has brought Carrock Mine into production. It is to be hoped that this course of events will not be responsible for the mine's future working.

The strike of the main veins, Smith, Harding and Emerson, can be clearly identified on site, to the north and south of Grainsgill Beck. Following the abandonment of the lease in 1988, the 1971 mill and associated buildings were cleared completely and the site, along with the tailings lagoon, was bulldozed and graded back to a close approximation of the original contours. The adit portals were destroyed and sealed, although mine drainage water still finds its way to day through the collapse at the Canadian Level, the main adit to the mine. Open stopes on the Harding Vein (north) were sealed with rails concreted over the stopes. The only remains of buildings left on the site are those on the south side of Grainsgill Beck, the concrete bases of hoppers constructed in 1913 by the Carrock Mining Syndicate.

A jackroll, or windlass, abandoned on Top Level, Paddy End Mine, Coniston. Jackrolls have been used since ancient times for raising and lowering men and equipment, and lifting ore and even water from the depths of the mine. They were still being used as recently as the early 1900s in the Cumbrian iron mining industry, particularly in the sinking of trial shafts where they were employed in raising kibbles of waste.

Photo: *Peter Fleming*

Many of the levels in ore mines were constructed on timber supports suspended above alarming drops below. This floor in the Hospital Level area of Coniston Mine has collapsed making access to further parts of the mine difficult.

Photo: *Mike Mitchell*

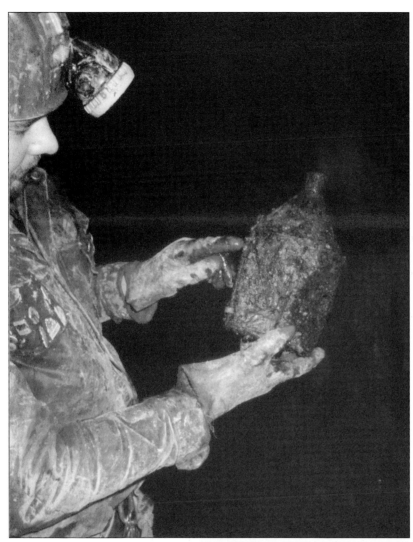

Even the smallest artefact has a story to tell. This rusting water container was discovered in Top Level at Paddy End, Coniston, when that part of the level was re-entered in 1987 by digging through a major collapse.

Photo: *David Bridge*

A pair of clogs also found in Top Level at Paddy End. It is said that when a mine was abandoned the miners often left a pair of clogs behind for luck.

Photo: *David Bridge*

Some of the large machinery left behind in an abandoned mine near Whitehaven. There were also large workshops and tyre changing depots catering for the several miles of underground roadways and workings.

Photo: *Mike Mitchell*

The open work below the holly tree is the original opening of the Grand Pipe, the site of one of the earliest discoveries of wad at Seathwaite in Borrowdale dating from the 16th century. In 1818 an experienced mine surveyor and geologist named John Farey was consulted. He made the extraction of the wad from the heart of the workings easier by bringing a tramming level out to day at the portal shown here. This became known as Farey's Stage.

Photo: *David Bridge*

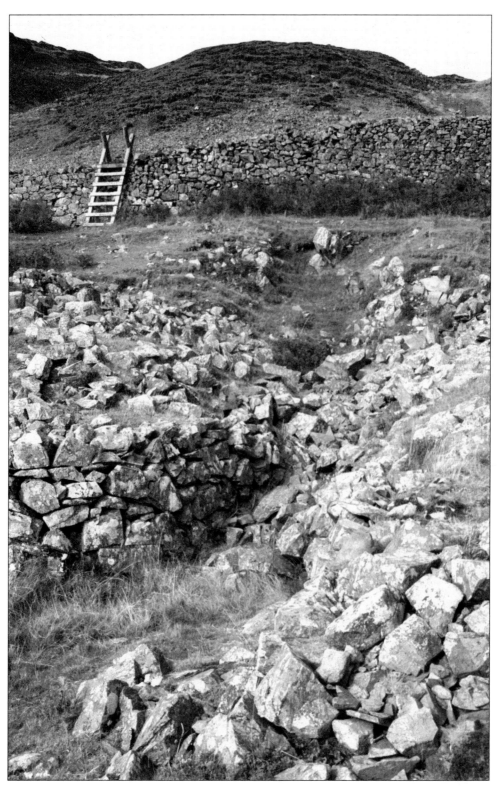

The other early discovery of wad known as the High Wadhole occurred higher up the fellside on Seatoller Common. Spoil from the workings can be seen above the boundary wall. In 1791 a level known as Harrison's Stage was driven below the wall to undercut these upper workings and a guardhouse built over the portal. Little remains of the structure today other than its foundations.

Photo: *David Bridge*

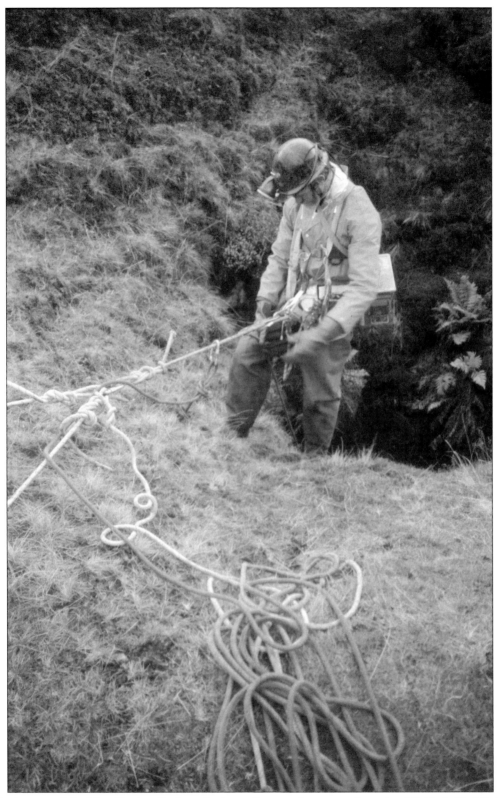

An early descent of the New Engine Shaft at Coniston Coppermines starts from the fellside in Red Dell. Some way down this shaft an old steel kibble was found and brought to the surface. It is now on display in Coniston's Ruskin Museum.

Photo: *Mike Mitchell*

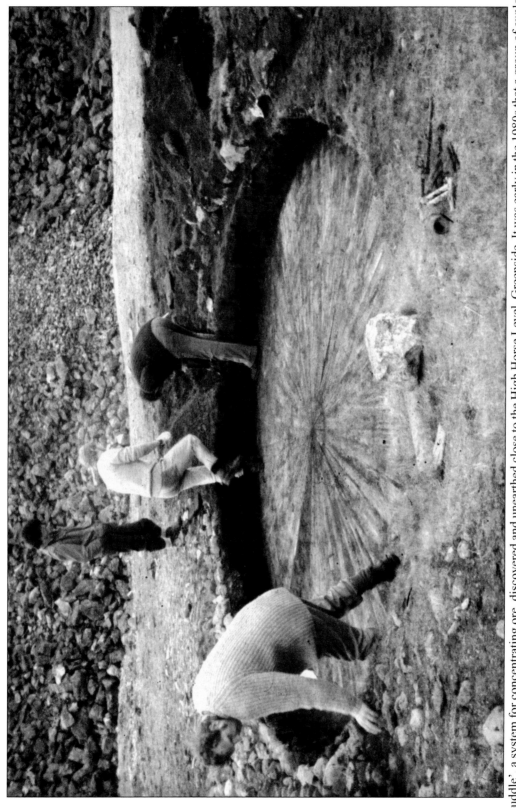

A 'buddle', a system for concentrating ore, discovered and unearthed close to the High Horse Level, Greenside. It was early in the 1980s that a group of explorers became aware of the possibility of this artefact beneath the surface and started to dig away the peat covering. Eventually the buddle was unearthed and found to be virtually intact. The roller crusher associated with it was found nearby, partly protruding from a spoil tip and this was also salvaged. After excavation the buddle was not left exposed for long. Within a fortnight the team had covered it with a large piece of polythene and replaced the peat to prevent deterioration.

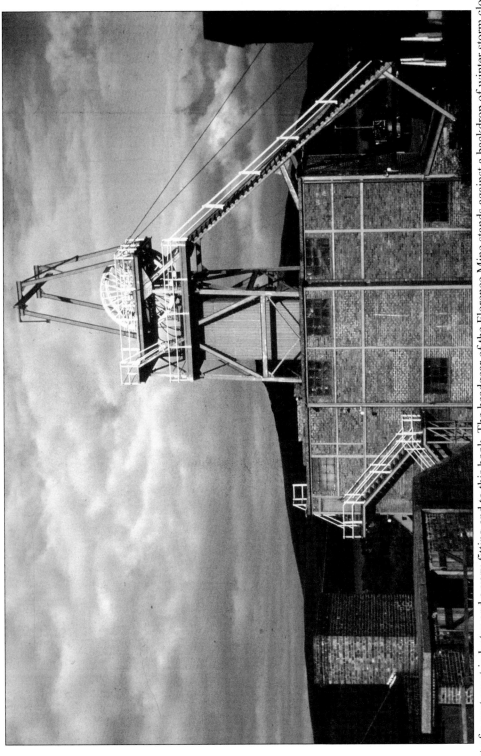

A remnant of a past great industry and a very fitting end to this book. The headgear of the Florence Mine stands against a backdrop of winter storm clouds over the Lakeland Fells.

Florence Mine is still working. It is the last deep ore mine in Europe. It is here that Gilbert Finlayson and his team have, for a number of years, been extracting extremely pure haematite from this part of West Cumberland.

In its heyday Florence employed 400 men. The haematite occurs in vein-like bodies within the limestone bedrock. The lower part of the mine is now flooded but at one time the shaft descended to 2000ft below the surface and the extensive roadway system associated with it is thought to extend for nearly 100 miles. Long may the pumps keep the water level down. Long may Florence Mine keep working. Long may Gilbert and his colleagues find a market for their haematite.

Acknowledgement – Alastair Cameron

It is difficult to know where to start to acknowledge the work put into this publication by individuals and organisations. The project to produce *Lakeland's Mining Heritage, The Last 500 Years* has been enormous and has taken years to complete.

Perhaps the first reference should be to Alen McFadzean, without whose vision this book would never have appeared. Alen realised the need to pull together within one cover the history of Cumbrian mining in articles and photographs. This first appeared as *Beneath the Lakeland Fells* in 1992, published by his own Red Earth Publications and now long out of print. Subsequently the ten authors who wrote the sections of *Beneath the Lakeland Fells* discussed with Alen the possibility of reproducing the book in an enlarged and updated form as a millennium publication. Alen magnanimously agreed to this suggestion and allowed the project to go ahead with what help he could give.

The second acknowledgement must go to **The Millennium Festival Awards to All** who also displayed considerable vision and foresight when they agreed to fund a large part of the publication. The work to secure the funding was carried out by Peter Fleming on behalf of the Society. Having obtained approval and funding the project then went ahead rapidly.

As Editor I would like to thank the section authors for responding rapidly to the need to update their text. I have to say that the articles in each chapter are both extremely readable and informative and will be a major point of reference for future scholars. Clearly, I should not mention any one of them as being outstanding. However, I am sure no one will complain if I refer to the chapter on Coal from the pen of ex-miner Ronnie Calvin. Ronnie has 'seen it all' and his writings reflect perfectly the hardship, anxiety and frequent despair associated with working in the West Cumberland coalfields. I should also like to mention Dave Blundell, the author of the chapter on Wolfram. David died in August 1994, three years after his original article was written. He was an outstanding and knowledgeable historian of the Lake District and a great person to be with on the fells. Mike Mitchell agreed to review Dave's article for this publication.

I must acknowledge the help given by the many experts in their fields. Thanks must go to Dave and Elizabeth Sewart who have carried out the origination of virtually the entire book. We are very fortunate that Dave's expert knowledge and sophisticated computer equipment is more or less at the forefront of technology. I won't forget the afternoon that we passed the draft of the entire book, text and photographs, to the printer in Cambridge, on a single CD-ROM.

I am also very grateful to Mike Mitchell for taking on the huge task of selecting photographs from the many contributors. This has taken many hours and both he and Dave Bridge subsequently scanned the entire collection onto Adobe PhotoShop software using their own equipment.

Many other people have been involved. John Hodgson of the National Park Authority has kindly produced the foreword for the book. Mark Simpson designed the front cover as part of his course at Kendal College into PhotoShop software, Peter Fleming has reviewed the Glossary and Bibliography and Nils Wilkes drew the 'chapter enders'. Cilla Cameron carried out a final proof-read of text, Karen Beer produced text for the cover fly, Angus Baillie helped by preparing proofs of parts of the book and Ian Matheson hosted the several 'book meetings' at his home in Coniston.

Glossary Of Mining Terms

ADIT – a horizontal tunnel driven into the hillside for access to the vein or to drain water from the mine.

BACK FILLING – waste rock which is dumped in a disused area of the mine to save the time and expense of bringing it out to day.

BALL MILL – revolving steel drum containing steel balls for crushing the ore.

BARGAIN SYSTEM – ritualistic system of paying miners on the amount of ore or slate raised from a predetermined section of ground; the miners worked in companies of three or more men, and the firm paid the companies as opposed to the individuals, at monthly or six-monthly intervals; this system was still being used in the Lakeland slate quarries in the 1940s.

BARYTES – or heavy spar, a sulphate of barium, mined extensively in the northern Lakes and Pennines.

BEARMOUTH – adit or level running into a hill, usually associated with coal mining.

BLACK JACK – mining term for sphalerite, the ore of zinc.

BLACK LEAD, BLACK CAWKE – Cumbrian terms for wad or graphite.

BLAST FURNACE – originally fuelled by charcoal, these furnaces were introduced to Cumbria in 1711 to produce iron from haematite ore.

BLENDE – mining term for sphalerite; see Black Jack.

BLOOMERY – a hearth, used since ancient times, and in the form of a clay dome, for processing haematite ore into workable iron.

BLOOMSMITHY – a technological advancement from the stringhearth; a modification of the later though possessing a forge hammer powered by a waterwheel.

BOUSE TEAM – ore bin, constructed of stone, into which ore from the mine is tipped before milling.

BORING RIG – apparatus for boring large-diameter holes through rock.

BROKEN GROUND – large scale subsidence associated with iron ore mining in Furness and the West Coast.

BUDDLE – apparatus for separating ore from veinstone.

CONCENTRATES – processed ore, usually non-ferrous, suitable for smelting.

CLOG – lump of quarried slate.

CLOSEHEAD – underground quarry for the working of slate.

COFFIN LEVEL – a narrow tunnel, coffin-shaped in section, usually dating to the Elizabethan period and driven without the use of explosives.

COUNTRY ROCK – naturally occurring rock, igneous, metamorphic, or sedimentary, in which the mineral vein is situated.

CROSS-VEIN OR CROSSCOURSE- a vein running counter to the major lodes in a mine.

CROSSCUT – a tunnel driven through country rock to intersect the vein or mineral deposit.

CRUSHING ROLLS – heavy iron rollers used during the primary stages of milling.

CUT AND FILL – mining method by which a stope is mined upwards and the waste rock is left underground in the floor of the working.

DAY – underground term meaning 'surface' or 'outside'.

DEADS – waste rock, usually stacked carefully underground to support the workings.

DIP – the angle of declination of a mineral vein or coal seam.

DRESSING – the reduction and sorting, by hand or machine, of veinstone into grades suitable for further processing; also the process of trimming roofing slates to their finished size.

DRESSING FLOOR – a cobbled area where dressing has taken place.

DRIFT – haulage or exploratory tunnel running along the vein or through mineralised ground.

FACE SHOVEL – large digger for use at the face of a quarry.

FALSE FLOOR – the floor of a tunnel made of timber and clay, constructed after the original floor has been mined away.

FATHOM – nautical measurement of six feet, widely used in the mining industry.

FEEDER (RUNNER) – an underground stream, frequently found in carboniferous limestone, and a curse to the iron miners of Furness.

FIREDAMP – explosive methane gas associated with coal mining.

FLAT – a body of ore, flat by nature, usually sandwiched between the bedding planes of sedimentary rock.

FLOTATION – a process separating the concentrated vein material by the application of oil rising through water, to which the minerals adhere.

FLOWSTONE – secondary mineralisation, forming curtains and cascades in the same manner that stalactites are formed.

FLUE – chimney stack, built along the ground to convey poisonous fumes from the smelt mills and discharge into the atmosphere, usually on the summit of the nearest fell.

FLUME – channel for conveying water.

GALENA – a sulphide of lead and the main lead mineral occurring in Cumbria.

GANGUE – secondary minerals in a vein, usually forming the matrix in which the more valuable minerals occur.

GIN – horse-powered capstan for raising ore or coal from a shaft.

GRIZZLEY – a series of bars set at intervals to grade the ore into determined sizes.

HAULAGE ROAD – tunnel along which tubs of ore or coal are hauled, usually by mechanical means.

HEAVY SPAR – miners' term for barytes.

HAEMATITE – the ore of iron.

HOPPER – a wooden chute fixed into the wall and roof of a level, through which ore is discharged to fill tubs from the workings above.

HORSE LEVEL – a major level where horses were used for hauling tubs of ore.

HUSH – a man-made gully down the side of a fell, excavated by the releasing of water from a dam; hushing was a mining method in its own right, applied to wash ore from mineral veins by the sheer force of water.

INCLINE – a tunnel driven upwards at an angle of usually thirty to fifty degrees from the horizontal; also a surface or underground tramway, constructed to raise or lower ore or slate from one plane to another, and powered by means of gravity, water or electricity.

JACKROLL – man-powered windlass for raising kibbles from a shaft.

JIGS – machines for separating ore from waste by means of agitation.

JUMPER – hand-held drilling steel.

KIBBLE – a large iron bucket for raising ore or equipment up shafts.

KIDNEY ORE – haematite ore in its usual form.

LEATS – courses cut into the fellside, or through rock, to channel water for the operation of waterwheels and other equipment.

LEVEL – horizontal access or drainage tunnel.

LODE – mineral vein.

MILL – industrial site for the processing of ore; also an underground ore-pass, constructed through waste rock, down which ore was thrown to hoppers below.

OLD MEN – miners' term for the miners of previous generations.

OPENCAST – method of mining mineral from an open quarry as opposed to an underground mine.

OVERBURDEN – the layer of unwanted material, usually glacial in origin, overlying a mineral deposit.

PELTON WHEEL – an enclosed wheel upon the periphery of which are fastened cups or small buckets which accept a jet of pressurised water; from the drive shaft, motion is transmitted to a variety of machinery.

PENCIL ORE – haematite ore manifesting in spike-like formations.

PILLAR – portion of the vein which is left in position to support the walls of a mine.

PINNEL – fine glacial boulder clay.

PIPE – graphite deposit, roughly cylindrical in shape.

PIT – a mine generally, but usually coal or iron.

PLUMBAGO – one of the many terms for wad or graphite.

PORTAL – the entrance to a level, usually constructed from local stone.

PUMP RODS – reciprocating rods of heavy timber, sometimes referred to as pit-work, conveying motion from a waterwheel or steam engine to the pumps at the foot of a shaft.

RISE – an internal shaft, usually blasted upwards through the rock to connect with a higher level.

ROYALTY – an area of land determined by a lease; also the payment demanded by the mineral owner on every ton of ore processed by the operator.

RUN-IN – a collapse in a level.

RUNNER – see feeder.

SCREENS – sieves for grading ore particles by size.

SEAM – coal deposit, usually horizontal in nature.

SETT – a timber frame to support the roof of a level; also a mineral royalty, an area of ground stipulated in a lease.

SHAFT – a hole, usually vertical or inclined at a steep angle, up which ore is raised, and down which miners descend to reach the lower levels of a mine.

SHOT HOLE – hole bored in rock to take explosives.

SMELTER – furnace for processing copper and lead ores.

SMIT – haematite ore in a greasy form, used since ancient times for marking sheep.

SOLE – the floor of a level.

SOP – large irregular body of ore.

SPOIL – waste rock tipped on the surface.

STAGE – tunnel or working horizon.

STEMMER – copper or brass rod used for loading shot holes with explosives.

STOPE – an area of the vein that has been removed.

STOPE AND FEATHERS – also called plug or slug and feathers; a chisel sandwiched between two steel wedges, or feathers, inserted into a hole and hammered, causing the rock to split by expansion; still used today in the quarrying of slate.

STRING – a vein or nib of mineral, usually secondary to a main vein.

STRINGHEARTH – technological advancement from the bloomery; the latter with a bellows powered by a waterwheel.

SUMP – a shaft sunk in the sole of a level; also a pool at the foot of a shaft in which the pumps are situated.

TAILINGS – fine waste from the milling process.

TOP-SLICING – the method by which haematite ore is removed from a sop, involving the removal of the ore slice by slice and the controlled subsidence of the ground above.

TRIAL – exploratory tunnel or quarry.

TRIBUTER – a miner working under the tribute system – similar in many ways to the bargain system.

VEIN – mineral body, usually of a vertical or near-vertical nature, striking through the rock for great distances and for great depths.

VUG – naturally occurring cavity in a vein, usually lined with fine mineral crystals.

WAD – local term for the graphite mined in Borrowdale.

WINDER – mechanism for winding ore from a shaft.

WOLFRAM – the ore of tungsten.

BIBLIOGRAPHY

Agricola, G De Re Metallica, 1556

Abraham G D, 'The Most Valuable Mine of Today', *The Autocar Magazine*, 1917

Adams J, *Mines of the Lake District Fells*, Dalesman, Clapham, 1988

Andrews M A, *The Birth of Europe*, BBC Books, London, 1991

Anon. 'Carrock Fell, UK Tungsten Mine with an interesting history is again producing concentrates', *Mining Magazine*, London, 1977

Anon. Coniston Mine an Unpublished Essay, Cumbria Record Office, Barrow-in-Furness, 1858

Ashley M, *The Golden Century*, 1969

Atkinson, R L, *Copper and Coppermining*, Shire Publications Ltd, 1987

Baur J, *Minerals, Rocks and Precious Stones*, Octopus, London, 1974

Becket J V, *Coal and Tobacco*, 1981

Bland R, Unpublished History of Coniston Coppermines, Cumbria Records Office, Barrow-in-Furness, 1978

Bolton J, *Geological Fragments of Furness and Cartmel 1869, 1869* (rep 1978)

Boon G C, 'An early Tudor Coiner's Mould and the Working of Borrowdale Graphite', *Trans Cumberland and Westmorland Antiquarian and Archaeological Soc, Vol 76 New Series*, Kendal, 1976

Bouch C M L, *Prelates and People of the Lake Counties*, 1948

Bouch C M L and Jones G P, *The Lake Counties 1500-1830*, Manchester University Press, Manchester, 1961

Briton J, Brayley E W, *The Beauties of England and Wales Vol 3*, 1805

Brownrigg R, Buttermere Green Slate, unpublished notes

Budworth J (Captain), *A Fortnight's Ramble in the Lakes in Westmorland, Lancashire and Cumberland by a Rambler* (2nd ed), 1795

Bulmer, *Directory of East Cumberland*, 1884

Bulmer T, *History, Topography and Directory of Cumberland*, 1901

Bun R, Waite P, Burnley R, *Cornish Mines Metalliferous and Associated Minerals*, University of Exeter, 1987

Burt R, Waite P and Burnley R, *The Cumberland Mineral Statistics 1845-1913*, University of Exeter, 1982

Burt R, Waite P, Burnley R, *The Lancashire and Westmorland Mineral Statistics 1845-1913*, University of Exeter, 1983

Burt R, Waite P, *Bibliography of the History of British Metal Mining*, University of Exeter, 1988

Camden W, *Britannia 1598*, trans P Holland, 1610

Cameron A D, 'Honister Slate Mine', *The Mine Explorer Vol III*, Cumbria Amenity Trust, 1989

Cameron A D, *Honister Slate Mine – A field Guide*, Cumbria Amenity Trust, 1990

Cameron A D, *Slate from Coniston*, Cumbria Amenity Trust, 1996

Cameron A D, *Slate from Honister*, Cumbria Amenity Trust, 1998

Campbell, 'Political Survey of Britain', Hutchinson W, *The History of the County of Cumberland Vol 2*, 1794 (rep 1974)

Clough R T, *The Lead Smelting Mills of the Yorkshire Dales and North Pennines*, Clough, Keighley, 1980

Collingwood W G, 'Elizabethan Keswick', *Trans Cumberland and Westmorland Antiquarian and Archaeological Soc, Series No 8*, Kendal, 1912 (rep 1987)

Collingwood W G, 'Germans at Coniston in the Seventeenth Century', *Trans Cumberland and Westmorland Antiquarian and Archaeological Soc, Vol 10 New Series*, Kendal, 1910

Collingwood W G, *Lake District History*, 1925

Collingwood W G, 'The Keswick and Coniston Mines in 1600 and later', *Trans Cumberland and Westmorland Antiquarian and Archaeological Soc, Vol 28 New Series*, Kendal, 1928

Collingwood W G, *The Lake Counties*, 1902, rev 1932, rev Rollinson W, 1988

Cooper M P, Stanley C J, *Minerals of the English Lake District Caldbeck Fells*, Natural History Museum Publication, London, 1990

Cowper H S, *The Oldest Register Book of the Parish of Hawkshead 1568-1704*, Bemrose & Sons 1897

Crosthwaite J F, 'Old Borrowdale', *Trans Cumberland Assn for the Advancement of Literature and Science, Pt I*, 1875-76

Crosthwaite J F, 'The Crosthwaite Registers', *Trans Cumberland and Westmorland Antiquarian and Archaeological Soc, Vol 2 Old Series*, Kendal, 1874-75

Cumberland Geological Society, *Proceedings Vol 2 parts 2 and 4*, 1967, 1969-70

Cumberland Geological Society, Shipp T (ed), *The Lake District – a Field Guide*, Unwin, London, 1982

Cumbria Amenity Trust Mining History Society, *The Mine Explorer Vols 1, 2, 3 & 4* 1984, 1986, 1989, 1994

Cumbria Amenity Trust Mining History Society, *Beneath the Lakeland Fells*, Red Earth Publications, 1992.

Cumbria Amenity Trust Mining History Society, *Newsletter No 23*, 1989

Cumbria Sites and Monuments Record

Davis R V, *Geology of Cumbria*, Dalesman, Clapham, 1979

Davies R, *John Wilkinson*, 1987

Dawson J, *Torver – The Story of a Lakeland Community*, Phillmore, 1985

Dewey H, Dines H G, 'Special Reports on the Mineral Resources of Great Britain Vol 1, Tungsten and Manganese Ores', *Memoirs of the Geological Survey*, HMSO, London, 1923

Dewey H, Eastwood T, 'Special Reports on the Mineral Resources of Great Britain Vol XXX', *Memoirs of the Geological Survey*, HMSO, 1925

Donald M B, *Elizabethan Copper*, 1955, Moon, Whitehaven, (rep 1989)

Dunham K C, Dines H G, *Barium Minerals in England and Wales*, Wartime Pamphlet No 46, Geological Survey of Great Britain, London, 1945

Eastwood T, *The Lake District Mining Field – The Future of nonferrous mining in Great Britain and Ireland*, London Institute of Mining and Metallurgy, London, 1959

Eastwood T, 'Special Reports on the Mineral Resources of Great Britain Vol 22, Ores of the Lake District', *Memoirs of the Geological Survey*, HMSO, London, 1921

Eastwood T, Dixon E E L, Hollingworth S E, Smith B, 'The Geology of the Workington and Whitehaven District', *Memoirs of the Geological Survey*, HMSO, 1931

Encyclopaedia Britannica, 1947

Farey J, Second Report of the Wad Mine in Borrowdale 1821 – Hunt R A, 'Historical Sketch of British Mining', *British Mining Bk 1*, 1887, Stanford, London, (rep 1978)

Fell A, *The Early Iron Industry of Furness*, 1908 (rep 1968)

Ferguson R S, *A History of Cumberland*, Elliot Stock, London, 1890 (rep 1970)

Fleming P, Coniston Copper Mines Rediscovered. Parts 1, 2 & 3. *The Mine Explorer*, CATMHS.

Fleming P, *Coniston Copper Mines*, The Ruskin Museum, Coniston, 2000.

Firman R J, 'Epigenic Mineralisation', Moseley F, *The Geology of the Lake District*, Yorkshire Geological Society, Leeds, 1978

Ford T D, Willies L, *Mining Before Powder*, Peak District Mining History Society, 1994

Forster W, *A Treatise on a section of the Strata from Newcastle upon Tyne to Crossfell*, Andrew Reid, Newcastle, 1883 (rep 1985)

Gentleman's Magazine, January 1751, Vol 21, 1751

Gentleman's Magazine, February 1751, Vol 21, 1751

Gibson A C, *Ravings and Ramblings Round Coniston*, Whinakers, London, 1849

Gilchrist D G, Moore C, 'Wicham Mines, Kirksanton, Millom', *The Mine Explorer Vol 2*, Cumbria Amenity Trust, 1986

Gilpin W, *Observations relative chiefly to Picturesque Beauty made in the Year 1772 on several parts of England, particularly the Mountains and Lakes of Westmorland and Cumberland Vol I* (2nd ed), 1778

Goodchild J G, Harkness R, *Trans Cumberland Assn for the Advancement of Literature and Science, No 8*, 1882-83

Gray T, *Journal of a Tour in the North of England*, 1769

Green W, *Guide to the Lakes Vol 2*, 1819

Hammersley G, Daniel Höchstetter the Younger, Memorabilia & Letters 1600-1639, *Copperworks & Life in Cumbria*, Stuttgart 1988.

Harris A, *Cumberland Iron: The Story of Hodbarrow Mine*, Bradford Barton, Truro, 1970

Harris A, Davies R B, The Hodbarrow Iron Mines, *Trans Cumberland and Westmorland Antiquarian and Archaeological Soc.* 1968

Hatchett C, 'A Tour through the Counties of England in 1796', Raistrick A (ed), *The Hatchett Diary*, 1967

Heller R L (ed), *Geology and Earth Sciences Source Book*, American Geological Institute, 1962

Hewer R E, 'Bannerdale Lead Mine', *British Mining No 25*, Northern Mine Research Society, 1984

Hewer R E, 'The Kelton & Knockmurton Iron Mines', *British Mining No 36*, Northern Mines Research Society, 1988

Hewer R E, 'The Trials of Ennerdale Region', *British Mining Memoirs No 37*, Northern Mine Research Society, 1988

Hewer R E, 'Iron Mines of Eskdale and Miterdale', *The Mine Explorer*, Cumbria Amenity Trust, 1984

Holland E G, *Coniston Copper: A History*, Cicerone, Milnthorpe, 1986

Holland E G, *Coniston Copper Mines: A Field Guide*, Cicerone, Milnthorpe, 1981

Holmes F M, *Miners and their Work Underground*, 1897

Hughes, *North Country Life in the 18th Century*, 1965

Hunt C J, *The Lead Mines of the North Pennines in the 18th and 19th Century*, Manchester University Press, 1970

Hunt I, *The Lakeland Pedlar*, Pinewood, 1974

Hunt R, 'A Historical Sketch of British Mining', *British Mining Bk 1*, 1887, (rep 1978)

Hutchinson W, *The History of the County of Cumberland Vol 2*, 1794, (rep 1974)

Jars M G, *Voyages Metallurgiques Vol 2*, 1780

Jefferson, *A History of Leath Ward*, 1860

Jollie, *Directory*, 1811

Jones A, 'Brewery Shaft, Nenthead', *The Mine Explorer Vol 1*, Cumbria Amenity Trust, 1983

Jones C D, 'Hartside Mines', *The Mine Explorer Vol 1*, Cumbria Amenity Trust, 1983

Kelly, *Directory*, 1894

Kelly, *Directory*, 1914

Kelly D, *The Red Hills*, Red Earth Publications, 1994

Kelly D, *The Red Earth*, Trinity Press, Barrow-in-Furness, 1996

Larousse Encyclopaedia of Modern History, 1964

Lefebure M, *Cumberland Heritage*, Gollancz, London, 1970

Lysons, *Magna Britannia Vol 4: Cumberland*, 1816

Mannix and Whellan, *History, Gazetteer and Directory of Cumberland 1847*, (rep 1974)

Marshall J D, Davies-Shiel M, *Industrial Archaeology of the Lake Counties*, David & Charles, 1969

Marshall J D, Davies-Shiel M, *The Lake District at Work Past and Present*

McFadzean A, 'Mining Methods on Lindal Moor', *UK Journal of Mines and Minerals No 6*, 1989

McFadzean A, *The Iron Moor*, Red Earth, Ulverston, 1989

McFadzean A, 'The Mines of Lindal Moor', *UK Journal of Mines and Minerals No 5*, 1988

McFadzean A, *Wythburn Mine and the Lead Miners of Helvellyn*, Red Earth, Ulverston, 1987

McMahon Moore A J, 'Carrock Fell Mine Cumbria', *Royal School of Mines Journal No 26*, London, 1977

Mitchell J G and Ineson P R, 'Potassium-Argon Ages from the Graphite Deposits and Related Rocks of Seathwaite, Cumbria', *Proc Yorkshire Geol Soc, Vol 40, Pt 3, No 24*, 1975

Nicolson W (Bishop), 'Letter to Dr Woodward, 5th Aug 1710', Nicholson J and Burn R, *The History and Antiquities of the Counties of Westmorland and Cumberland Vol 2*, 1777

Otley J, 'Account of the Black Lead Mine in Borrowdale', *Memoirs, Literary and Philosophical Society of Manchester, Ser 2, Vol 3*, 1819

Otley J, *A Concise Description of the English Lakes and Adjacent Mountains* (6th ed), Keswick, 1837

Otley J, *A Descriptive Guide to the English Lakes and Adjacent Mountains* (8th ed), 1849

Parson W, White W, *A History, Directory and Gazetteer of Cumberland and Westmorland 1829*, (rep 1976)

Parnell J, 'Genesis of the Graphite Deposits at Seathwaite in Borrowdale, Cumbria', *Geological Mag Vol 119*, 1982

Pennant T, 1772, Hutchinson W, *The History of the County of Cumberland Vol 2*, 1794, (rep 1974)

Postlethwaite J, *Mines and Mining in the English Lake District* (3rd ed), Whitehaven, 1913, (rep 1975)

Pough A, *A Field Guide to Rocks and Minerals*, Constable, London, 1970

Prospectus for the Cumberland Black Lead Mine Company, 1859

Raistrick A, *History of Lead Mining in the Pennines*, Longmans, London, 1965

Raistrick A, *Two Centuries of Industrial Welfare*, Moorland, Hartington, 1977

Rawnsley H D, *Past and Present in the English Lakes*, 1916

Read H H, *Rutley's Elements of Mineralogy*, (26th ed), 1970

Robinson T, *An Essay toward a Natural History of Cumberland and Westmorland*, 1709

Rollinson W, *Life and Tradition in the Lake District*, Dent, London, 1981

Sedgwick A, 'Suggestions on the Origin of Plumbago', *Quart J of the Geol Soc, Vol 4*, 1848

Shackleton E H, *Lakeland Geology*, Dalesman, Clapham, (4th ed), 1973

Shaw W T, *Mining in the Lake Counties*, Dalesman, Clapham, 1972

Simonim L, *Mines and Miners*, 1868

Slater D, *Tungsten – Mineral Dossier No 5*, Mineral Resources Consultative Committee, HMSO, London, 1973

Smith B, 'Iron Ores', *Special Report on the Mineral Resources of Great Britain Vol Vlll*, HMSO, London, 1924 (rep 1988)

Smith B W, *The World's Great Copper Mines*, 1967

Snowdonia National Park Study Centre, Peter & Susan Crew (Ed), *Early Mining In the British Isles*, SNPSC, Plas Tan y Bulch, 1990

Sopwith T, *An Account of the Mining District of Alston Moor, Weardale and Teesdale*, Davidson, Alawick, 1833 (rep 1984)

Strens R G J, 'The Graphite Deposit of Seathwaite in Borrowdale, Cumberland', *Geol Mag, Vol 102, No 5*, 1965

Sutton S, *The Story of Borrowdale*, 1960

Tylecote R F, *A History of Metallurgy*, 1988

Tyler I, *Force Crag: The History of a Lakeland Mine*, Red Earth, Ulverston, 1990

Tyler I, *Greenside – A Tale of Lakeland Miners*, Red Earth, Ulverston, 1992

Tyler I, *Honister Slate – The History of a Lakeland Slate Mine*, Blue Rock Publications, 1994

Tyler I, *Seathwaite Wad*, Blue Rock Publications, 1995

Tyler I, *Thirlmere Mines – The Drowning of the Valley*, Blue Rock Publications, 1999

Tyler I, *Gypsum in Cumbria*, Blue Rock Publications, 2000

Victory County History for Cumberland, 1905

Wallace W, *Alston Moor, Its Pastoral People, Its Mines and Miners*, Davis, Newcastle, 1986

Ward J C, 'The Geology of the Northern Part of the English Lake District', *Memoir of the Geological Survey*, 1876

Weis P L, Friedman I, Gleason J P, 'The Origin of Epigenetic Graphite: Evidence from Isotopes', *Geochemica et Cosmochimica Acta Vol 45*, 1981

Whellan, *History and Topography of Cumberland and Westmorland*, 1860

Williams M, *The Slate Industry*, Shire Publications, 1991

Williams N, 'The Story of Carrock Mine', *University of Sheffield Geological Society Journal Vol 7*, 1979

Willies L, *Lead and Lead Mining*, Shire Publications, 1982

Young B, *Glossary of the Minerals of the Lake District and Adjoining Areas*, British Geological Survey, Newcastle, 1987

Index